"MISS PEACH . . . a sophisticated funny about a naive young schoolmarm and her class of irrepressible youngsters . . . overrun by small fry with the incisive viewpoint that makes grownups gasp in real life."

—*Newsweek*

Newsweek likes MISS PEACH—see the comment above.

Readers of 200 newspapers like MISS PEACH–and look for her daily and Sundays.

We like MISS PEACH—and consider it a privilege to publish this collection of her adventures.

You'll like MISS PEACH—how could you help it?

Miss Peach

by MELL.

Introduction by

Al Capp

Cindy Jean Briggs

PYRAMID BOOKS ▲ NEW YORK

For the Peaches in My Life

MISS PEACH

A PYRAMID BOOK
published by arrangement with Prentice-Hall, Inc.

PRINTING HISTORY

Prentice-Hall edition published 1958
Second printing, October 1958

Pyramid edition published September 1962

Library of Congress Catalog Card Number 58-13531

Printed in the United States of America

PYRAMID BOOKS *are published by Pyramid Publications, Inc., 444 Madison Avenue, New York 22, New York, U.S.A.*

INTRODUCTION

There once was (and still is) a bustling institution in New York called Capp Enterprises, which ruthlessly exploited me, and which I owned.

Capp Enterprises produced dolls, comic books, games, greeting cards and cereal package covers, all either in the likenesses of "Li'l Abner" characters or bearing their likenesses on the covers.

Several artists generally named Mort, Marty, or Mel were employed there to copy my stuff. Neither Mort nor Marty made much of an impression on me then, but Mel did.

He never seemed to smile much when he looked at my "Li'l Abner" strips.

Mel smiled when he looked at me.

I must say this for him; he never actually laughed at me. He just smiled.

Well, now I know why, and as you go through this book you will know why.

If you compare these illustrated short stories (which, in our time, are dismissed from literary consideration by being called comic strips), you will notice an unusually attractive quality in both the words and the pictures—namely, that there isn't much of either.

If you look at the work by any of the others of us, you will see that we all draw a lot more and write a lot more than Mel does. But none of us says any more, or even hardly as much.

There is, you will see, an awful lot of this book which is blank space. And yet, in Mel's hands, that space isn't empty. It all throbs with such emotions as anguish, embarrassment, defeat, disappointment, despair—practically everything, in fact, that makes us happy when we see it happening to other people.

And that was why, a few years ago, Mel didn't smile at my work. He smiled at me because although I was, for that moment, the boss, I hadn't discovered the

priceless secret of our art that he had—that if you were a humorist with more understanding than most other humorists, you could fill emptiness with delight, and silence with wit.

This is Mel's genius.

Al Capp

PREFACE

There are three ways to create a comic strip. One is to have a syndicate call you up and ask you to whomp up something special for them. Another is to survey the field of existing comics, decide what's missing, and then offer the void-filler on the market.

The third way is the least exciting. That is to have an idea insinuate itself into your subconscious, there germinate and grow until it cracks through the crust of your consciousness.

At this stage, you must put the idea down on paper or it will push out through your skull like grass through a concrete highway.

That's how "Miss Peach" came to be.

I don't know when the school-teacher comic-strip seed was first planted in my mind, but the first green shoot appeared in the weed-patch (that I laughingly refer to as my consciousness) some three years before she ever saw daylight on my drawing board. And it was at least five years before Miss Peach appeared in the public prints.

Launching the comic strip, however, is only the beginning of the cartoonist's troubles. The really important character and theme development takes place during the first year or so of actual publication.

The personalities of Miss Peach, her pupils, the principal and the faculty of the Kelly School emerged slowly and gradually. Today some of them are quite different from the way I originally planned them. Indeed, certain characters that I thought would figure prominently no longer even exist in the cast!

All of which is to show that the comic strip artist is not really his own boss. His characters, like Frankenstein's monsters in miniature, soon take over and start running his strip.

This may make his job easier (and he's in favor of

that) but it plays hob with his self-respect and professional aplomb.

After the initial period of character establishment, a peculiar phenomenon of fiction writing comes into play. This is the strange tendency of characters to write their own story. There are moments when the writer feels more like a chronicler than an author. The pen and ink personalities become so real and strong to him that he can control them only with the greatest effort.

So, I now find myself in the humiliating position of being told what to do, seven days a week (in full, rich color on Sundays) by a classroomful of big-mouthed, articulate, and sophisticated kids. I even get an occasional kick in the pants from a hyperactive octogenarian named Miss Crystal. I'm a figurehead. A puppet governor.

These, my characters, have created for themselves a veritable jungle of squads, clubs, and committees called the Kelly School. Such a school really could exist nowhere in our present academic climate except in the mind of a cartoonist and on the comic pages of the newspapers that see fit to run it.

There's a bright side for me, though. Drawing this comic strip is my personal palliative for the incurable disease of Growing Up. Besides, as one of the least distinguished students ever to sneak through the New

York City educational system, I may, when I can emotionally detach myself, secretly enjoy the spectacle of a group of modern, atom-oriented kids running the self-expression gamut, sniping at their teachers' self-respect, vanity, sanity, and professional reputations in the process, while nonetheless carrying off Honors and Awards by the gross!

But when, finally, even _my_ sense of propriety and dignity is outraged, I need only turn to Miss Peach. She can be reasoned with. She understands. She's soft-spoken, gentle, unbelievably sweet, and has a heart of pure gold. And her I can still handle—I think. At any rate, Miss Peach leavens, for me, the lump of cynicism that we must so often swallow.

In spite of the fact that she's never taken (repeat: taken) a punchline, and has probably spoken the least dialog of any character in the comic strip that bears her name, she's very, very definitely its leading light.

She's the star.

MEL

Mel Lazarus
New York City

Incidentally, when we were selecting the 193 strips to reprint in this book, the editors felt that one man's opinion would not suffice. It was therefore decided to pass the proof-books around among four of us representing the syndicate and the publisher. The idea, of course, was to use those 193 strips upon which we all concurred. But when we tallied up, we found that we'd checked off a grand total of 400 strips.

I had checked with a blue pencil, Harry Welker with a red pencil, Bob Gillespie used a green pencil, and Berney Geis an orange one.

But one morning, lo and behold! I arose to find 193 strips checked with a purple pencil. Those are the ones I'm about to show you.

After all, who can argue with a purple pencil? ML

CONTENTS

NOW
TURN THE
BOOK SIDEWAYS,
STUPID!

Meet Freddy

My kid's father is a cartoonist . . . and Freddy's father is a psychiatrist. But despite both these dreadful handicaps, each of them is the best adjusted pupil in his respective class.

Freddy is so well adjusted, he doesn't even mind sitting in the last seat in the classroom. In fact, he actually likes it because it automatically guarantees him the last comment in the strip, which, in turn, guarantees him an existence free from "back talk." Which is probably why he's so well adjusted.

YES- EVEN BONNIE PRINCE CHARLIE GOES TO SCHOOL... AND I UNDERSTAND HIS TEACHERS GIVE HIM EXCELLENT MARKS!
HUMPH!
WHY SHOULDN'T THEY GIVE HIM GOOD MARKS— HIS MOTHER IS THE ENTIRE QUEEN OF ENGLAND!!
LET'S BE FRANK, MISS PEACH— WOULDN'T MY MARKS BE GOOD IF I COULD DANGLE THE TOWER OF LONDON OVER YOUR HEAD?
MELL
WILL THE MONITORS DISTRIBUTE THE SCHOOL NEWSPAPER, PLEASE?
HEARYAR! HEARYAR! GETCHA WUXTRA! GETCHA...
JUST HAND THEM OUT, IRA, YOU DON'T HAVE TO HAWK THEM
I SEE THAT KINDERGARTEN 3 WON THE POTSY CHAMPIONSHIP AGAIN.
WELL, SURE! THEY'VE GOT ALL THE VETERAN PLAYERS.
DID YOU READ MY LETTER TO THE EDITOR ABOUT THE SCHOOL BUILDING APPROPRIATION?
MUST YOU TAKE CREDIT FOR EVERY ANONYMOUS LETTER THEY PRINT?
OUR CLASS COLUMN IS BLANK! AREN'T YOU SUPPOSED TO BE OUR CLASS CORRESPONDENT?
I REPORT THE NEWS AS I SEE IT.
MELL

YES, FRANCINE, YOU **DO** HAVE LOVELY HAIR!
-ONLY IT DIDN'T GROW VERY LONG THIS WINTER...
EVERYBODY KNOWS THAT HAIR GROWS FASTER IN WARM WEATHER
YES! WHEN I WAS IN FLORIDA MY HAIR GOT **VERY** LONG!
THAT'S AN OLD WIVES' TALE! ACTUALLY, THE HOT SUN SHRINKS YOUR HEAD SO YOUR HAIR JUST **LOOKS** LONGER.
MELL

COACH
MR. MUSSELMAN, WE HAVE A QUESTION TO ASK YOU...
MAN -TO- MAN...
IS IT TRUE THAT WHEN WE GROW UP WE'LL RATHER **GO OUT WITH GIRLS** THAN PLAY BASKETBALL ?
IF SO, **HOW COME ?** GOING OUT WITH GIRLS ISN'T AS **HEALTHY** AS PLAYING BASKETBALL !!
WITH GIRLS, YOU HAVE TO MOSTLY **SIT STILL AND LOOK DOPEY** ALL THE TIME, DON'T YOU ?
YOU CAN'T COME IN, MISS PEACH! THIS IS MAN TALK...
MELL

IT SAYS IN THE LATEST **WILDLIFE BULLETIN** THAT THE FEDERAL GOVERNMENT WILL NO LONGER PROTECT THE THISTLE BIRD!
WHO DOES THE FEDERAL GOVERNMENT THINK IT IS?
SILLY! IT REPRESENTS THE SOVEREIGN PEOPLE OF THE UNITED STATES...
...AND IF THEY SAY THAT SWEET LITTLE BIRD ISN'T WORTH CONSERVING, THAT'S THAT!
WELL, **I** DON'T AGREE...
...AND IN THE FUTURE, I'LL THANK THE **FEDERAL GOVERNMENT** AND THE **SOVEREIGN PEOPLE OF THE UNITED STATES** TO SPEAK FOR THEMSELVES!
MELL

YOU'RE JUST IN TIME, MISS PEACH. WE'RE PLAYING **PSYCHOANALYST!**
FREDDY'S A WHIZ AT THIS.
YES HE CURES YOU SO FAST IT MAKES YOUR HEAD SPIN.
WELL, YOU'RE SUFFERING FROM DEPRESSIONS, FIXATIONS, REPRESSIONS, NEUROSES, FRUSTRATIONS, SUPERIORITY, INFERIORITY AND OEDIPUS COMPLEXES, REGRESSIONS AND FEAR OF BEING REJECTED.
GO HOME AND READ MY NEW BOOK, **"HOW TO KEEP ONE JUMP AHEAD OF YOUR MIND"** AND YOU'LL BE ALL RIGHT IN THE MORNING.
MELL

BIG COMPANIES SOMETIMES HAVE **CONFERENCES** WHERE EVERYBODY WRITES DOWN ANY **SILLY THING** THAT COMES TO THEIR MIND...
BUSINESS NEWS
-NO MATTER **HOW** SILLY...
-THEN THEY LOOK THROUGH THE LIST OF SILLY THINGS-
- AND VERY OFTEN THEY FIND **MONEY-MAKING IDEAS** AMONG THEM!
SO **WE** JUST TRIED IT!
AND DO YOU THINK YOU CAME UP WITH ANYTHING THAT'S **WORTH MONEY?**
WHAT'S THE GOING PRICE FOR A **LIST OF SILLY THINGS?**
MELL

AFTER FRANCINE TELLS US ABOUT HER TRIP TO THE ZOO, CLASS, WE'LL HAVE OUR **ARITHMETIC TEST.**
WELL, FIRST WE FED A PEANUT TO THE ELEPHANT, THEN WE WENT TO THE MONKEY HOUSE...
NOT SO FAST!
DETAILS! DETAILS!
YOU'RE SKIMPING!
GETTING BACK TO THAT **PEANUT....**
WAS IT A DOUBLE OR A SINGLE?
MELL

HAVE YOU THOUGHT ABOUT YOUR CLASS PLAY, CHILDREN?
YES, MISS PEACH. THIS TIME WE'RE GOING TO PRODUCE A SPECTACULAR!
IT'LL BE VAST! COLOSSAL! FABULOUS!
WITH GREAT SCOPE! COLOR! PAGEANTRY!
BUT WHAT WILL WE USE FOR A THEME?
HOW ABOUT THE "STORY OF THE ANT?"
MELL
SINCE THIS IS THE LAST BANK DAY OF THE SCHOOL YEAR, MISS PEACH, CAN WE TAKE OUR MONEY OUT?
YES, BUT WHY?
WHILE WE'RE AT CAMP ALL SUMMER THE BANK MIGHT SPEND OUR MONEY!
WHY WOULD THEY?
SUMMER'S COMING, RIGHT? HOT WEATHER, RIGHT? ICE CREAM TASTES GOOD TO YOU? WELL, BANKERS ARE HUMAN, TOO, YOU KNOW!!
HE'S RIGHT. NO SENSE PUTTING TEMPTATION IN THEIR PATH!
I'LL TAKE MY 85 CENTS, PLEASE.
MELL

MARCIA HAS THINGS ALL FIGURED OUT... —WHEN SHE GROWS UP SHE'S GOING TO BE **THE PRESIDENT'S WIFE!**
HE'S ALREADY GOT ONE!
NOT THIS ONE, SILLY..! I MEAN THE PRESIDENT WHO'S PRESIDENT WHEN I GROW UP!
THAT FUTURE PRESIDENT IS JUST A LITTLE BOY RIGHT NOW, DEAR!
Bless Our Hobby Room
THAT'S RIGHT: MARCIA'S BEING VERY RIDICULOUS. HOW DOES SHE KNOW HE'LL EVEN ASK HER?
IN FACT. I **WON'T.**
MELL

FREDDY HAS SOLD YOU ALL **INSURANCE POLICIES?**
YES, MISS PEACH! —BUT I DON'T SEE ANY **BENEFITS...**
—IT SAYS NOTHING ABOUT **COVERAGE...**
—OR HOW WE **COLLECT...**
—IN FACT, THERE'S **NO PROTECTION** AT ALL!
WHAT KIND OF **INSURANCE POLICY IS** THIS ?!
FREDDY INSURANCE CO. SOLD OUT
IT GIVES YOU **"PEACE OF MIND."** WHAT MORE DO YOU WANT FOR 3¢?
MELL.

TELLER
TODAY IS SCHOOL BANK DAY...
-BUT WE WANT TO SEE WHAT YOU PEOPLE DO WITH OUR MONEY!
1ST NATIONAL BANK
THE BANK INVESTS IT IN GOOD, SOUND ENTERPRISES THAT OFFER A PROFITABLE RETURN!
IN OTHER WORDS, YOU PLAY AROUND WITH OUR MONEY...
- I WOULDN'T SAY THAT! WE PAY YOU INTEREST ON YOUR DEPOSITS...
UM-HUH! WELL, BETTER STAY ON YOUR TOES...
YES. -YOU NEVER KNOW WHEN WE'LL DROP IN UNANNOUNCED...

HOW'S THE HALLOWE'EN PARTY DOING, MISS PEACH?
FINE, MISS CRYSTAL! AND WAIT TILL YOU SEE THE COSTUMES! —THEY RUN FROM THE SUBLIME TO THE RIDICULOUS!
ALL RIGHT! WHO'S THE WISE GUY TRYING TO LOOK RIDICULOUS?
MELL

THE BOYS WILL NOW TELL US ABOUT THEIR GOPHER PATROL ACTIVITIES LAST MONTH!
LAST MONTH WE COLLECTED SIX OLD TOYS..
GOPHER PATROL ACTIVITY CHART
-WE FOUND HOMES FOR THREE STRAY DOGS!.
-AND HELPED FOUR OLD LADIES CROSS THE STREET..
-THEN WHAT DO THESE MEAN?
THEY'RE FOUR OLD LADIES WHO HELPED US CROSS THE STREET..
WE HAVE A MUTUAL ASSISTANCE PACT WITH ALL THE OLD LADIES IN TOWN...
MELL.

Dear Miss Peach:
Just a note to thank you
for the wonderful job you're doing
with our son Freddy's education.
Having our boy's future in your hands
must be a tremendous burden!
We are ever so grateful for such
fine teachers as yourself - teachers
who are able to bear this great
responsibility.
With sincere relief,
Mr. and Mrs. Foster
THIS IS A VERY NICE NOTE FROM YOUR PARENTS, FREDDY. PLEASE THANK THEM FOR ME!
I WILL, MISS PEACH!
-IT TAKES MOM AND POP OFF THE HOOK NICELY, DOESN'T IT?
MELL.

-YOU'RE DESIGNING A MODERN HOUSE, CHILDREN?
YES, MISS PEACH! -IT'S A RANCH HOUSE! IT'S GOT A WASHING MACHINE...
-BARBEQUE PATIO, TWO-CAR GARAGE...
-BUILT-IN WALL OVEN, TILE BATHS...
STORM WINDOWS, FULL BASEMENT...
-AND IT ONLY COSTS $139,000.00
GOODNESS! WHAT MAKES YOUR RANCH HOUSE SO EXPENSIVE?
-THE HERD OF CATTLE AND THE OIL WELL...
MELL

YOU'RE GIVING EACH OTHER HOME PERMANENTS?
YES, MISS PEACH... THIS IS THE AGE TO START BEAUTY TREATMENTS AND THINGS...
-A GIRL SHOULD WATCH HER APPEARANCE...
-LATER IN LIFE IS TOO LATE...
-RIGHT, MISS CRYSTAL?
HOW DO I LOOK, BOYS?
-LIKE THE FOREMAN IN A WITCH FACTORY...
MELL

Marcia is a Stinker

The phrase, "Marcia is a stinker," has never been uttered in Miss Peach's classroom nor scrawled on any fences in proximity thereto. The reason for this is simple: Marcia <u>is</u> a stinker.

She's also the unquestioned social leader of the class. She gets all the juiciest parts in the class plays by virtue of the fact that she writes, produces, directs and casts them.

Marcia's very definitely a leader-type. Life behind Marcia is exciting, but don't stand in her way.

Dear Miss Peach:
I had forgotten that today is a school holiday, and I made plans to attend a luncheon.
Since you're really so used to having children around, I don't think you'll mind keeping an eye on my daughter Marcia at your home this afternoon.
Thanks so much!
Mrs. Mason
YOUR MOTHER WOULD LIKE ME TO LOOK AFTER YOU THIS AFTERNOON?
YES, MISS PEACH. SHE SAYS YOU CAN HAVE "CARTE BLANCHE" WITH ME–
THAT'S FRENCH. IT MEANS I CAN DO ANYTHING I WANT!
MELL

WHY IS YOUR BUNK THE LAST ONE TO BE CLEANED, GIRLS?
IT'S MARCIA'S FAULT, MISS PEACH...
–SHE'S OUR OFFICIAL SWEEPER...
–BUT SINCE SHE STARRED IN THE CAMP PLAY, SHE REFUSES TO SWEEP..
–UNLESS WE STREW ROSE PETALS IN HER PATH...
Bless Our Bunk
–AND ROSE PETALS ARE HARD TO SWEEP UP..
MELL

DREAMS ARE SIMPLY YOUR IMAGINATION WORKING WHILE YOU SLEEP.
DREAMS COME TRUE, MISS PEACH!
I FOUND A DOLLAR AFTER I DREAMED I WOULD...!
IMAGINE THAT!
I ONCE DREAMED I WENT TO THE CIRCUS, AND THE NEXT DAY MY FATHER TOOK ME!
GOSH! DREAMS DO COME TRUE!
LAST NIGHT I DREAMED I WAS THE ENTIRE QUEEN OF THE WORLD AND I HAD ALL THE CANDY AND TOYS AND EVERYTHING.
...!!
DON'T FORGET YOUR OLD FRIENDS, YOUR MAJESTY...
MELL.

HOW'S YOUR CLUB MEETING COMING ALONG, CHILDREN?
NOT SO GOOD, MISS PEACH. PRESIDENT MARCIA HAS THE FLOOR...
—AND SHE REFUSES TO RECOGNIZE ANYONE ELSE!
MADAME PRESIDENT
—BLAH, BLAH, BLAH, BLAH, BLAH, BLAH...
DON'T BOTHER GOING TO THE MEETING, ARTHUR. MARCIA WON'T RECOGNIZE ANYBODY!
(GULP!) AFTER ALL THESE YEARS SHE'S BECOME A COMPLETE STRANGER?
MELL.

WHAT ARE YOU DOING, CHILDREN?
WE'RE PLAYING "BABBLE," MISS PEACH! —AND I'M WINNING!
YOU SURE ARE, MARCIA!
THAT LAST WORD OF YOURS WAS A BEAUT!
YOU SCORED 75 POINTS ON IT!
I'LL HAVE TO REMEMBER THAT ONE...
—WHAT DOES "ZYXZQX" MEAN ANYWAY?
MELL

WHY CAN'T I DANCE IN THE SCHOOL SHOW, MARCIA?
—I HAVE CLASS...
—GRACE...
—PLENTY OF RHYTHM...
—SHOWMANSHIP...
—AND STYLE.
WELL, YOU TALK A GOOD DANCE, IRA...
—DROP AROUND FOR AN AUDITION SOME TIME.
MELL.

WE BOARD OUR PLANE FOR HOME IN 5 MINUTES, CHILDREN!
IDLEWILD AIRPORT
I LIKE TO SIT UP FRONT IN AN AIRPLANE!
—SO THAT IF A PROPELLOR FALLS OFF, FOR INSTANCE, **YOU'LL** BE THE FIRST TO KNOW?
--AND THEN YOU'LL BE ABLE TO TELL THE OTHER PASSENGERS ABOUT IT, HUH?
-YOU'LL HAVE **BIG NEWS** FOR THEM, RIGHT?
DON'T SMIRK AT HER! -**EVERYBODY** LIKES TO FEEL IMPORTANT...
MELL

-WHOEVER PUT MARCIA'S LUNCH IN THE WASTEBASKET OWES HER AN APOLOGY...
I DIDN'T DO IT, MISS PEACH, BUT I WISH I HAD..
-ME NEITHER, BUT IT WAS A **GREAT** IDEA...
WHY DIDN'T **I** THINK OF IT?
-OR **ME.** DARN IT...
-OR **ME...**
WELL, **SOMEBODY** DID IT..
HMMM.... -WHO DO I KNOW THAT HATES ME, BESIDES EVERYBODY?
MELL

THAT MARCIA BURNS ME UP!
—ME, TOO...
—ALWAYS TALKING ABOUT HOW **GORGEOUS** SHE IS...
-ARE YOU HAPPY BEING A **BEAUTIFUL CHILD,** MARCIA?
(SIGH!) -NOT ALWAYS, MY DEAR...
—IT'S NO FUN BEING DRAGGED AROUND BY ONE'S FORMER PEDIATRICIAN.
-AS A **SAMPLE,** YOU KNOW...
MELL.

—A PERSON CAN BE VERY NICE, BUT STILL HAVE THEIR LITTLE **"IDIOSYNCRASIES."**
THAT'S TRUE, MISS PEACH...
—TAKE MARCIA, FOR EXAMPLE...
- SHE'S GOOD, WARM...
—HUMBLE, SWEET...
—KIND AND GENTLE...
-BUT EVEN **SHE** HAS ONE TEENCHY LITTLE "IDIOSYNCRASY"...
-SHE HATES PEOPLE..
MELL.

HOW ARE YOUR SEED SALES, MISS PEACH?
THE CHILDREN DON'T SEEM TO WANT BEAN SEEDS..
YOU'RE NOT SELLING THEM, MISS PEACH.
-YOU'VE GOT TO USE PROMOTION. -WATCH US!
GET YOUR BEAN SEEDS WHILE THEY LAST!
-GROW BEAN STALKS!
-MEET GIANTS..!
-FIND GOLDEN GEESE!
I'LL TAKE SOME OF THOSE!
SAVE ME SOME!
MELL
MARCIA'S ALWAYS BRAGGING ABOUT ALL THE FRIENDS SHE'S GOT...
WELL, IT'S NICE TO HAVE MANY FRIENDS, CHILDREN...
-BUT MARCIA DOESN'T REALIZE THAT EVERYONE REALLY HATES HER...
OH, IS THAT SO?
-I'LL HAVE YOU KNOW MY CIRCLE OF FRIENDS IS GROWING CONSTANTLY!
THAT'S NO CIRCLE OF FRIENDS, MARCIA...
-YOU'RE BEING SURROUNDED..
MELL

M-MARCIA DID IT, MISS PEACH...
—SHE TRIED TO MAKE US SAY SHE'S THE SWEETEST CHILD IN CLASS...
I CAN'T BELIEVE THAT MARCIA WOULD STRIKE ANYONE...
—SHE WOULD, MISS PEACH...
—AND I KNOW WHY, TOO... —SHE FEELS INSECURE, THAT'S WHY!
—WITH A PUNCH LIKE SHE'S GOT, WHY SHOULD SHE FEEL INSECURE?
MELL

MARCIA MADE ME SAY I LOVE HER...
—SHE MADE ME TELL HER HOW SWEET SHE IS...
—SHE MADE ME SAY SHE'S MY BEST FRIEND...
—I'M TRUE-BLUE WITH A HEART OF GOLD, RIGHT, LESTER?
YES, MARCIA... —YES, YOU ARE...
—YOU'RE THE BEST-LOVED ENEMY WE'VE GOT...
MELL

Introducing Ira ...who attracts criticism

Ira attracts criticism the way month-old candy draws flies. He's got more faults than he could ever be bawled out for.

One of them, for example, is the fact that month-old candy attracts Ira. The flies who got there first have to fight him off. He's a glutton.

Worse than that, he's a coward. Not withdrawn, nervous or phobic—just plain yellow. But he owns up, at least, and cheerfully admits these things. And for that, we can't help loving the little rat.

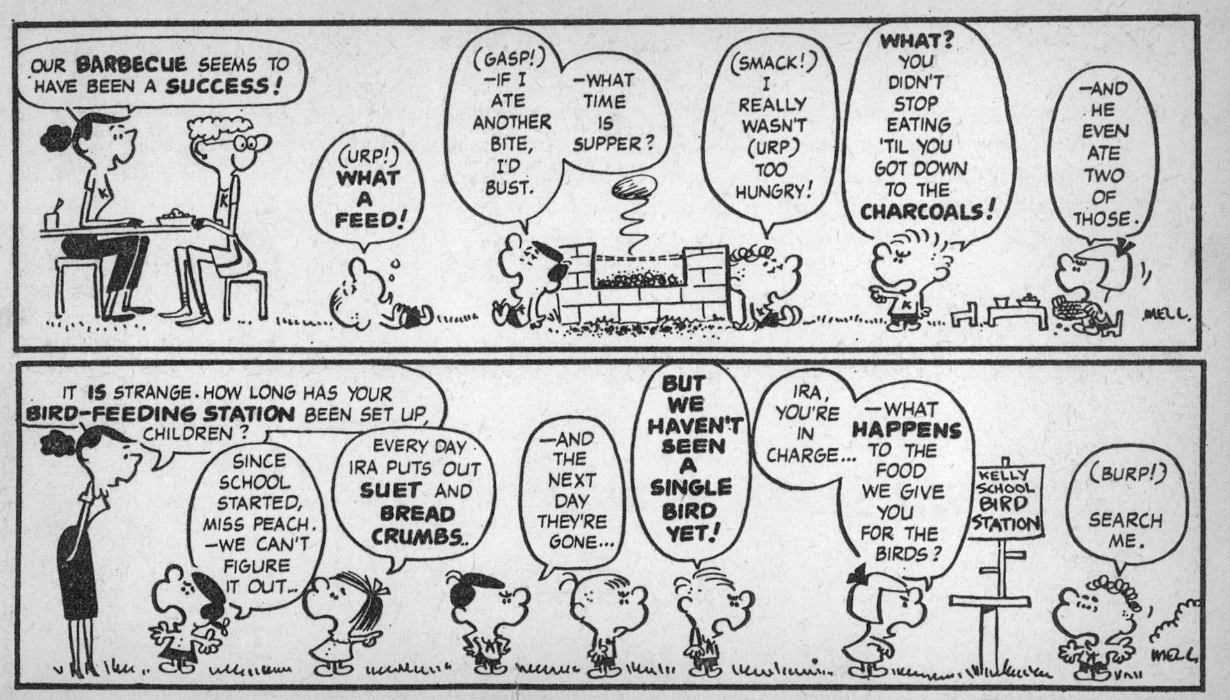
OUR BARBECUE SEEMS TO HAVE BEEN A SUCCESS!
(URP!) WHAT A FEED!
(GASP!) —IF I ATE ANOTHER BITE, I'D BUST.
—WHAT TIME IS SUPPER?
(SMACK!) I REALLY WASN'T (URP) TOO HUNGRY!
WHAT? YOU DIDN'T STOP EATING 'TIL YOU GOT DOWN TO THE CHARCOALS!
—AND HE EVEN ATE TWO OF THOSE.
MELL.
IT IS STRANGE. HOW LONG HAS YOUR BIRD-FEEDING STATION BEEN SET UP, CHILDREN?
SINCE SCHOOL STARTED, MISS PEACH. —WE CAN'T FIGURE IT OUT...
EVERY DAY IRA PUTS OUT SUET AND BREAD CRUMBS..
—AND THE NEXT DAY THEY'RE GONE...
BUT WE HAVEN'T SEEN A SINGLE BIRD YET!
IRA, YOU'RE IN CHARGE...
—WHAT HAPPENS TO THE FOOD WE GIVE YOU FOR THE BIRDS?
KELLY SCHOOL BIRD STATION
(BURP!) SEARCH ME.
MELL

THANKS FOR THE GRAPES, ARTHUR!
YOU'RE WELCOME. THEY'VE BEEN CLUTTERING UP MY POCKET FOR THREE WEEKS NOW...
THREE WEEKS IN YOUR POCKET?
IRA'S EATING HIS!
(GULP!) HE'LL EAT ANYTHING!
IRA, THOSE GRAPES WERE IN ARTHUR'S POCKET FOR THREE WEEKS!
(SLURP!) YES, (SMACK!) —THREE VINTAGE WEEKS!
MELL,

YOU MAY START YOUR BIRTHDAY PARTY NOW, IRA.
SAY! THAT'S RIGHT! IT'S IRA'S BIRTHDAY AND HE PROMISED US A PARTY!
HE CHANGED HIS MIND.
NO PARTY.
WHY NOT, IRA? YOU PROMISED, DIDN'T YOU?
—YOUR MOTHER SAID IT WAS OKAY, DIDN'T SHE?
SHE GAVE YOU CANDY FOR THIRTY CHILDREN, DIDN'T SHE?
(BURP!)
YES.
MELL.

IN HONOR OF THANKSGIVING, IRA'S MOTHER HAS SENT YOU EACH A CHOCOLATE TURKEY!
ONE BOX CHOCOLATE TURKEYS
THANK YOU, IRA... -HEY!! WHERE'S MY TURKEY'S HEAD?!
MY TURKEY'S TAIL HAS BEEN CHEWED OFF!
WHAT'S WITH THE NO FEET?
IRA, HOW COME ALL THESE TURKEYS ARE HALF-EATEN?
I DON'T KNOW... -I GUESS MY MOTHER GOT THEM ON SALE...
BURP!
MELL
-AND SO, LOUIS PASTEUR'S GERM THEORY WAS OF GREAT BENEFIT TO HUMANITY!
-PASTEUR, REED...
-SALK, CURIE...
-THEY ALL MADE GREAT CONTRIBUTIONS TO HUMANITY!
MAKES YOU FEEL KIND OF SILLY AND USELESS, DOESN'T IT, IRA?
NOT ME, KIDDO!
-WHO DO YOU THINK GOT BANANA SANDWICHES PUT ON THE LUNCHROOM MENU!?
MELL

BEES!!
I'M SURROUNDED BY BEES!!
HELP! I'M SCARED STIFF!!
YOU REALLY HAVE NOTHING TO WORRY ABOUT, IRA...
-SURE... THEY'LL ONLY STING IF YOU MOVE -STAND STOCK STILL AND YOU HAVE NOTHING TO FEAR.
-BESIDES THEY'D HAVE TO STING YOU A THOUSAND TIMES TO KILL YOU..
-AND BEES CAN'T COUNT WORTH A DARN...
NOW DON'T YOU FEEL FOOLISH MAKING ALL THAT FUSS FOR NOTHING?
MELL

BEING AFRAID OF CERTAIN THINGS DOESN'T MAKE ONE A "SISSY", CLASS...
MISS PEACH IS RIGHT!
MOST PEOPLE ARE ONLY AFRAID OF CERTAIN THINGS...
-LIKE HEIGHT...
-OR DARK PLACES.
NOT IRA... -HE'S AFRAID OF ALMOST EVERYTHING!
THAT'S TRUE.
-I'M WHAT YOU CALL A FREE-LANCE COWARD...
MELL.

-SO REMEMBER, CHILDREN, A QUART OF MILK PLUS REGULAR BRUSHING EACH DAY EQUALS GOOD TEETH!
ISN'T DOCTOR WHITING A NICE MAN?
-HE SURE IS...
-DOCTOR WHITING HAPPENS TO BE MY DENTIST.
-I'M ONE OF HIS FAVORITE COWARDS...
MELL

WHAT'S THE TROUBLE, CLASS?
COACH
-MARCIA CALLED IRA A SISSY...
-BECAUSE HE'S AFRAID TO PUT THE GLOVES ON WITH HER.
-DON'T YOU KNOW BY NOW THAT IRA IS A COWARD, MARCIA!
YES, I DO.
-THEN WHY DON'T YOU TAKE THAT INTO CONSIDERATION BEFORE YOU GO CALLING ME A SISSY?
MELL

THE KELLY SCHOOL
Dear Mrs. Brown,
During our class play yesterday your son Ira was engaging in horseplay backstage. His clowning resulted in the scenery falling on stage. This disrupted the show and upset the children, so we had to call off the rest of the play.
I would like to make certain that Ira's tomfoolery does not continue. Therefore, will you please come to see me so we can discuss this problem?
Yours truly,
Miss Peach
MOTHER, DURING OUR CLASS PLAY I BROUGHT THE HOUSE DOWN -- I REALLY STOPPED THE SHOW! MISS PEACH WOULD LIKE TO TALK TO YOU ABOUT MY FUTURE AS A COMEDIAN!
MELL

HOW'S YOUR WORLD MAP COMING ALONG, CLASS?
-SILLY IRA FORGOT TO PUT IN GREENLAND...
I-ER- DID NOT FORGET! I LEFT IT OUT ON PURPOSE.
YES, I DID..! -I DON'T LIKE GREENLAND!
IT'S NOT FAIR TO SAY THAT! YOU'VE NEVER EVEN BEEN THERE!
-THAT'S A TERRIBLE ATTITUDE TO HAVE TOWARDS GREENLAND...
YES! I'M SURE GREENLAND GIVES HIM THE BENEFIT OF THE DOUBT...
MELL

I TOLD THE CLASS THEY COULD BRING TOYS FROM HOME TODAY..
THAT'S THE BIGGEST STUFFED BEAR I EVER SAW..!
WHY DID YOU BRING THAT BIG THING, IRA...
-JUST TO BE FUNNY?
FUNNY? -YOU THINK GETTING ON THE BUS WITH THIS THING WAS A JOKE?
MELL
DOESN'T THE CHILDREN'S GIFT SHOW GOOD TASTE, MR. GRIMMIS?
INDEED IT DOES! IT'S SO DIGNIFIED, I BELIEVE I'LL WEAR IT TO THE SCHOOL BOARD MEETING TONIGHT!
PRINCIPAL
IT HAS A SPECIAL FEATURE, MR. GRIMMIS...
-IT GLOWS IN THE DARK...
-IF YOU CAN GET THE SCHOOL BOARD TO TURN OUT THE LIGHTS FOR A MINUTE...
-THE TIE WILL LIGHT UP AND SAY "OH YOU BABY DOLL, YOU"...
MELL

Women Will Talk

What does the hair-ribbon set talk about within the sanctity of the dormitory or the sewing circle? The same secret intimacies of life that the big girls do, of course, only more so.

BEING A "WIFE" IS BETTER THAN BEING JUST A "DAUGHTER".
YES, BUT A "MOTHER" OUTRANKS A "WIFE".
"GRANDMOTHER" IS A GOOD DEAL. "GRANDMOTHER" GETS THE MOST RESPECT OF ALL...
...BUT IF YOU'RE A "GRANDMOTHER" YOU'RE ALSO A "MOTHER-IN-LAW"... -AS A RULE.
HMMM. YOU'RE RIGHT. LET'S JUST QUIT WHEN WE GET TO "MOTHER"...
...UNTIL SUCH TIME AS THEY CHANGE THE RULE.
MELL
"—AND YOU HAVE BEEN LEFT OUT OF THE CROWD'S FUN BECAUSE YOU DON'T KNOW HOW? OUR OFFER OPENS UP A NEW WORLD OF OPPORTUNITY FOR YOU; OPENS THE WAY TO A RICHER, HAPPIER, MORE PROFITABLE LIFE. YOUR FRIENDS WILL GASP WITH ENVY! START TODAY TO ENJOY THE BENEFITS WE..."
Elvis
KAMP E KAZOH
Bless Our Bunk
WHAT ARE YOU DOING UP AT THIS HOUR, GIRLS?
VASSAR
MARCIA'S READING US TO SLEEP, MISS PEACH...
GO ON, MARCIA. IT'S JUST GETTING GOOD...
MELL.

MISS CRYSTAL IS HOMELY, ISN'T SHE?
YES.
CAN SHE COOK?
NO.
CAN SHE SEW?
NO.
"MISS" MEANS SHE'S SINGLE, DOESN'T IT?
YES.
SMALL WONDER.
MELL
CHILDREN, THE SNOW IS SO DEEP THAT WE MUST REMAIN IN SCHOOL UNTIL THE SNOW PLOW CAN CLEAR THE YARD...!
WE'RE SNOWED IN? GOODY!!
-IT'LL BE GREAT FUN!!
-WE'LL SING SONGS...
Bless Our Home Room
-AND PLAY GAMES AND DANCE...
-WE'LL HAVE A REAL NICE, COZY SOCIAL AFTERNOON!
WHO WITH?
MELL

-OF COURSE MY MOTHER IS A YOUNG WOMAN..
-SHE'S ONLY THIRTY!
SINCE WHEN IS THIRTY A YOUNG WOMAN?
SORRY TO DISILLUSION YOU, LINDA, BUT YOUR MOTHER IS NO LONGER A "YOUNG WOMAN"..
—WE MIGHT SAY SHE FALLS INTO THE YOUNGER GROUP OF "OLD WOMEN"...
—BUT THAT'S ABOUT THE BEST WE CAN DO FOR THE POOR OLD THING ...
MELL
YOUR MOTHER'S AN AMATEUR SHOPPER NEXT TO MY MOTHER...
OH, REALLY? —WHAT MY MOTHER FORGOT ABOUT SHOPPING..
—YOURS HASN'T LEARNED YET.
-MY MOMMY CAN SHOP RINGS AROUND BOTH YOUR MOMMIES.
YOU HAVEN'T SEEN ANYTHING 'TIL YOU'VE SEEN MY MOTHER SHOPPING IT UP!
WELL, WHEN MY MOTHER GOES DOWNTOWN, THEY BOARD UP THE WINDOWS...
—SHE REALLY SHOPS UP A STORM!
MELL

The Betrothal of Marcia and Ira

Ira doesn't love Marcia. His mute acceptance of his "engaged condition" to Marcia is a tribute to his philosophical, fatalistic viewpoint, and especially to his cowardice. He fully realizes that, as the mate of Marcia the Miserable, he will be dragged through life by one arm. But he's too chicken to object really.

Perhaps he feels safe and secure thereby, like the pheasant "saved" from the foxes by the lioness.

—THE GIRLS HAVE RAFFLED OFF IRA?
YES, MISS PEACH! WE FOUND OUT HE'S GOT $2.65 IN THE SCHOOL BANK..!
—SO WE DREW STRAWS FOR HIM, AND MARCIA WON!
—AS SOON AS THEY GRADUATE FROM COLLEGE, THE LITTLE MONEY-BAGS IS ALL HERS!
HERE HE COMES NOW!
SHAKE HANDS WITH MARCIA, IRA. YOU TWO ARE GETTING MARRIED.
THAT'S RIGHT, IRA.
NOTHING PERSONAL, YOU UNDERSTAND..
MELL

—NOW THAT MARCIA WON IRA IN THE RAFFLE, THEY'RE ENGAGED.
-ISN'T A WOMAN SUPPOSED TO CHANGE HER FIANCÉ OVER?
THAT'S RIGHT, MARCIA! FOR INSTANCE— HIS HAIR IS TOO CURLY. MAKE HIM PLASTER IT DOWN...
-HE EATS TOO MUCH PUT HIM ON A DIET...
-AND HIS POSTURE IS TERRIBLE. MAKE HIM STRAIGHTEN UP...
YOU HEARD THEM, IRA, DEAR. START CHANGING...
CAN I KEEP MY OLD FEET?
—THEY HAPPEN TO FIT ALL MY SHOES...
MELL

MARCIA WON IRA IN A RAFFLE, SO THEY'RE GOING TO GET MARRIED IN FIFTEEN YEARS...
(GULP!) -CONGRATULATIONS ON YOUR TERRIBLE MISFORTUNE, IRA...
MARCIA, I DON'T THINK IRA'S FRIENDS WILL BE A GOOD INFLUENCE ON HIM...
YOU'RE RIGHT! I'LL HEREBY FORBID HIM TO PLAY WITH THEM ANYMORE!
HOPE
Wedding Announcement Samples
FIFTEEN YEARS WITH NO FRIENDS!
-GOLLY! -HE'LL BE A SIMPERING, WITLESS HULK OF A MAN...
-IN SHORT, A PERFECT HUSBAND...
MELL

MARCIA AND IRA ARE ENGAGED TO BE MARRIED?
YES, MR. GRIMMIS, -DON'T THEY MAKE A LOVELY COUPLE?
WE'VE ONLY GOT FIFTEEN YEARS TO PLAN THE WEDDING.
-SO RIGHT NOW WE'RE WORKING ON THE ANNOUNCEMENT.
BIG MARRIAGE!
-JUNE 19TH, 1973-
MARCIA -VS- IRA
POPULAR YOUNG LIGHTWEIGHT SHREW.
-SHORT TEMPER! -LOUD MOUTH! -MEAN STREAK!
CROWD-PLEASING FAVORITE.
-STUBBORN! -FAST ON HIS FEET! -SNEAKY!
"FOR BETTER OR FOR WORSE"
MELL

WHEN MARCIA AND IRA ARE MARRIED
-SHE'LL SHOW HIM WHO'S BOSS!
-SHE'LL REALLY CRACK THE WHIP!!
-SHE'LL RUN HIM RAGGED!
-SHE'LL BREAK HIS SPIRIT IN SHORT ORDER!!
-AND WHAT'S MORE, I'LL TEACH YOU THE MEANING OF FEAR!
BUCK UP, IRA... -AS LONG AS SHE PROMISES TO LOVE, HONOR AND OBEY, WHAT DO YOU CARE?
MELL
WHAT IS MARCIA DOING?
SHE'S EXPLAINING TO IRA WHAT THEIR MARRIAGE WILL BE LIKE...
-SHE SAYS AS LONG AS HE TREATS HER LIKE A QUEEN, THEY'LL BE NO TROUBLE...
-AND I EXPECT YOU TO PLACE ME ON A PEDESTAL... -UNDERSTAND, DEAR?
MARCIA
MELL
SO WHAT, IRA? -SHE'LL HAVE TO COME DOWN FOR MEALS...!

—IRA SHOULDN'T BE ANGRY JUST BECAUSE HIS **BIRTHDAY GIFT** IS **BELATED...**
SEE, IRA?
—WHAT DIFFERENCE DO A FEW WEEKS MAKE?
—AFTER ALL, IT'S THE SPIRIT THAT COUNTS...
RIGHT! SO PLEASE ACCEPT THIS TOKEN OF OUR AFFECTION AND ESTEEM...
—OR I'LL BASH IT OVER YOUR FOOL HEAD!
MELL.

OH, IRA... —IN REGARD TO OUR ENGAGEMENT...
WE'RE **NOT** ENGAGED...
—I SIMPLY REFUSE TO GO THROUGH WITH IT...
—I CAN'T EVEN STAND THE SIGHT OF YOU...
I WON'T BE ENGAGED AND THAT'S FINAL!
—HAVE YOU SEEN THE RING I PICKED OUT?
MELL

ISN'T IT NICE THAT MARCIA AND IRA ARE **STILL ENGAGED?**
IT SURE IS. —ENGAGEMENTS DON'T ALWAYS LAST, YOU KNOW.
THAT'S TRUE. -MY COUSIN CELIA HAD TO CALL OFF **HER** ENGAGEMENT...
—SHE USED TO **SNEEZE** WHENEVER HER FIANCE WAS AROUND...
-SHE WAS ALLERGIC TO HIM...
(SOB!) —WHY CAN'T A SCIENTIFIC MIRACLE COME TO **MY** RESCUE, SOMETIME?
MELL
I WOULDN'T MARRY YOU IN A MILLION YEARS, MARCIA...
—YOU'RE **FUNNY-LOOKING!**
I'M WHAT?
—YOU'RE (GULP!) NOT SO BAD...
—YOU'RE REALLY **NICE LOOKING,** IN FACT...
-YOU'RE VERY PRETTY...
—YOU'RE GORGEOUS!!
—IF YOU HAVE NOTHING ELSE, IRA, YOU HAVE GOOD TASTE.
MELL

Clubs, Squads, and Committees

An average of three committees per pupil—that's the latest count at the Kelly School. This midget bureaucracy is threatening to engulf the nation.

IRA IS SICK AT HOME, CHILDREN. DO WE HAVE ANY VOLUNTEERS FOR A **HAPPINESS SQUAD** TO VISIT HIM AFTER SCHOOL?
I'LL VOLUNTEER! IRA SAYS BOYS ARE HEALTHIER THAN GIRLS —AND NOW I WANT TO **GLOAT.**
COUNT ME IN, MISS PEACH! IRA GOT A NEW CHEMISTRY SET FOR BEING SICK, AND I'M ITCHING TO GET MY HANDS ON IT!
PUT ME ON THE **HAPPINESS SQUAD,** TOO! MAYBE I'LL COLLECT THAT 3 CENTS THE RAT OWES ME!
MELL

WHAT'S HAPPENING??
YOU'RE JUST IN TIME, MISS PEACH... —WE'VE FORMED A **MUTUAL SELF-IMPROVEMENT SOCIETY...**
—WE HELP EACH OTHER TO SEE OUR **WEAK POINTS** IN A **FRANK** AND **HONEST MANNER...**
YOU LACK UNDERSTANDING!
WALTER, YOU'RE A WRETCH!
FREDDY, YOU'RE NASTY!
STUART, YOU'RE A SHOW-OFF!
IRA, YOU'RE A NINNY!
MARCIA, YOU'RE A SLOPPY DRESSER!
SHEILA, YOU'RE A BIG MOUTH!
YOU'RE A DUMMOX!
MELL

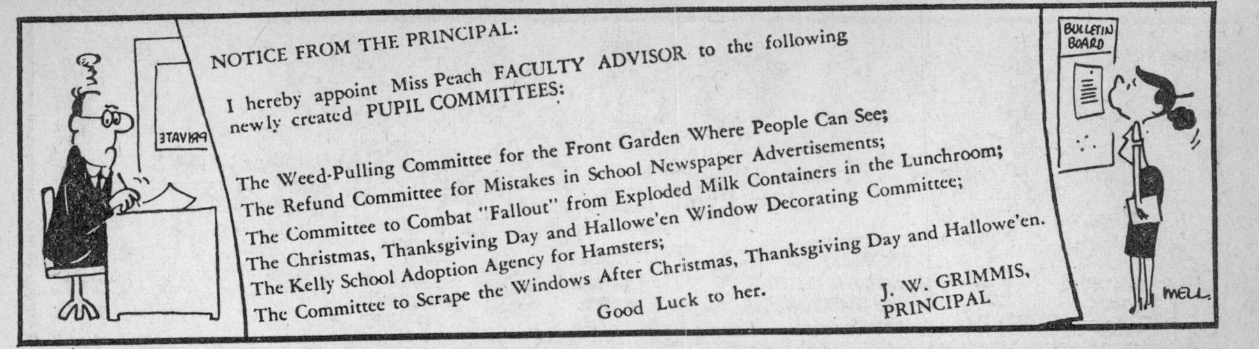
PRIVATE
BULLETIN BOARD
NOTICE FROM THE PRINCIPAL:
I hereby appoint Miss Peach FACULTY ADVISOR to the following newly created PUPIL COMMITTEES:
The Weed-Pulling Committee for the Front Garden Where People Can See;
The Refund Committee for Mistakes in School Newspaper Advertisements;
The Committee to Combat "Fallout" from Exploded Milk Containers in the Lunchroom;
The Christmas, Thanksgiving Day and Hallowe'en Window Decorating Committee;
The Kelly School Adoption Agency for Hamsters;
The Committee to Scrape the Windows After Christmas, Thanksgiving Day and Hallowe'en.
Good Luck to her.
J. W. GRIMMIS,
PRINCIPAL
MELL

OUR BUNK WON THREE AWARDS THIS SUMMER!...
—THE "V" FOR VOLLEY BALL THE "H" FOR HIKING AND THE "F" FOR FROG-COLLECTING!
KAMP V KELLY
KAMP H KELLY
KAM F
SO WHAT? OUR BUNK WON THE "B" FOR BIRD-NAMING THE "L" FOR LAUNDRY THE "S" FOR SWEETNESS... THE "W" FOR WEEDLESSNESS THE "C" FOR CUTENESS THE "T" FOR TRAIL-BLAZING THE "G" FOR GENEROSITY...
—AND RIGHT NOW WE'RE TRYING FOR THE "E" FOR ENTHUSIASM AND THE "R" FOR RESTRAINT...
—AND THAT'S A VERY DIFFICULT COMBINATION!
MELL

NOTICE FROM THE PRINCIPAL:
I have noticed the distinct lack of sweetness among the pupils of our school, so I have decided to institute the following program:
Hereafter, every morning at ten o'clock the Kelly School will enjoy a "Sweetness Break". A hand-picked team to be known as the "Sweetness Squad" will wander through the school spreading sunshine and joy.
By order of the principal J.W. Grimmis.
BULLETINS
WE'D LIKE TO VOLUNTEER FOR THAT MISS PEACH. WE'RE DEDICATED TO THE IDEA OF SPREADING HAPPINESS...
—AND WE DON'T MIND MISSING ARITHMETIC, EITHER.
—BIG MOUTH!
MELL
GEE THEY MADE ME FEEL GOOD!
—NOW IT'S FRANCINE'S TURN!.
KELLY SCHOOL SWEETNESS SQUAD
SMILE, FRANCINE, SMILE!
WE LOVE YOU!
WHAT A CUTE DRESS!
YOU'RE ADORABLE!
YOU HAVE FRIENDS, DEAR!
YOU'RE A DARLING!
MR. GRIMMIS THINKS THIS "SWEETNESS SQUAD" IDEA IS WORKING OUT FINE. HE DOESN'T SEE ANY HARM IN EXPERIMENTING.
NEITHER DID DR. JEKYLL.
MELL

THERE GOES THE "SWEETNESS SQUAD," SPREADING SWEETNESS THROUGHOUT THE SCHOOL...
-FOR THE FIFTH STRAIGHT DAY-
YOU'RE A FINE BOY, LESTER!
BE HAPPY!
YOU'RE LOOKING WELL!
BLESS YOUR HEART!
CHEER UP!
WE LOVE YOU!
YOU'RE A REAL DOLL!
SWEETNESS SQUAD
WHAT DO YOU EXPECT AFTER FIVE DAYS... -SINCERITY?
MELL

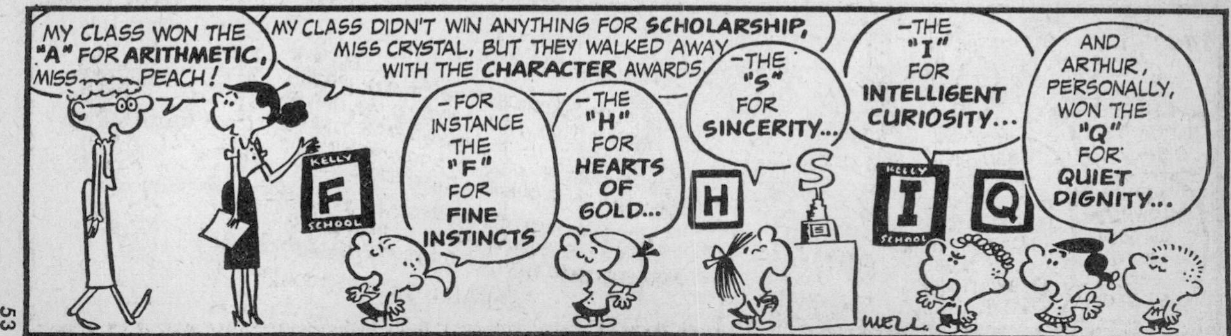
MY CLASS WON THE "A" FOR ARITHMETIC, MISS PEACH!
MY CLASS DIDN'T WIN ANYTHING FOR SCHOLARSHIP, MISS CRYSTAL, BUT THEY WALKED AWAY WITH THE CHARACTER AWARDS
-FOR INSTANCE THE "F" FOR FINE INSTINCTS
-THE "H" FOR HEARTS OF GOLD...
-THE "S" FOR SINCERITY...
-THE "I" FOR INTELLIGENT CURIOSITY...
AND ARTHUR, PERSONALLY, WON THE "Q" FOR QUIET DIGNITY...
KELLY F SCHOOL
H
S
KELLY I SCHOOL
Q
MELL

JOINT COMMITTEE TO STRAIGHTEN EVERYTHING OUT
-MR. GRIMMIS, I'M AFRAID THE "JOINT COMMITTEE TO STRAIGHTEN EVERYTHING OUT" IS HERE TO SEE YOU AGAIN...
PRINCIPAL
-I'M LEAVING A LITTLE EARLY TODAY, MISS ELLIOT...
MELL
-NOW OUR NEXT COMPLAINT IS ABOUT THE ARITHMETIC TEST LAST WEEK...
"JOINT COMMITTEE TO STRAIGHTEN THINGS OUT."
-WHY, OH WHY DO YOU PLAGUE ME WITH ALL THESE PETTY COMPLAINTS? WHY MUST YOU BRING THEM TO ME?
MR. GRIMMIS PRINCIPAL
YOU'RE SUPPOSED TO TAKE CARE OF THINGS AROUND HERE, AREN'T YOU?
-THAT'S YOUR JOB, ISN'T IT, MR. GRIMMIS?
-HERE WE'RE TRYING TO THROW A LITTLE BUSINESS HIS WAY...
-AND THAT'S THE THANKS WE GET...
MELL

Arthur Out of Orbit

Arthur's not really stupid. He's got the same brains as anybody else, his classmates agree. As Freddy put it, "he was launched successfully but never quite got into orbit."

ARTHUR STRIMM! WHY DID YOU GIVE ME THIS LETTER TO READ?
I WAS ABSENT YESTERDAY, MISS PEACH, AND YOU SAID WHEN WE'RE ABSENT WE HAVE TO BRING A LETTER FROM HOME...
...THAT WAS THE ONLY LETTER I COULD FIND.
COLLECTION DEPART
LAX'S DEP'T. STOR
Dear Mrs. Strimm:
We have tried . . .
in as pleasant a manner as possible to secu
payment of your long overdue account.
But, it appears that we have failed, and it
now becomes necessary to refer your account t
our attorneys. I don't like to do this, be-
cause it will mean needless embarrassment, in-
convenience and extra expense to you.
Very truly yours,
Collection Depar
MELL

WHAT ARE YOU PLAYING, CHILDREN?
IT'S A NEW WORD GAME, MISS PEACH!
EVERYBODY WRITES DOWN A FIVE-LETTER WORD...
...ENDING IN "B" OR BEGINNING WITH "J"...
WITH ONLY TWO CONSONANTS UNLESS YOU HAVE A DOUBLE VOWEL FOR THE 2ND AND 3RD LETTERS...
THE WINNER IS THE ONE WITH THE MOST "Z"S", UNLESS THERE'S AN "L" AFTER "R" IN WHICH CASE YOU TRUMP YOUR OPPONENT'S "W'S", IF ANY. YOU START, ARTHUR.
......
A HOW MANY LETTER WORD?
MELL

I'M HAPPY TO SEE THAT YOU ALL PLAN TO GO THROUGH COLLEGE!
YES, MISS PEACH, BUT COLLEGE IS VERY EXPENSIVE. I EXPECT TO WORK MY WAY THROUGH...
ME, TOO! I'LL BE A WAITER IN THE COLLEGE LUNCHROOM.
I'LL PLAY FOOTBALL. THE SALARY WILL HELP ME THROUGH COLLEGE!
I'LL HAVE TO SELL ENCYCLOPEDIAS, BUT ARTHUR HERE IS THE LUCKY ONE...
HIS SOCIAL SECURITY WILL GET HIM THROUGH COLLEGE!
MELL
YOU WANT TO EXPEL ARTHUR FROM THE CLASS? SURELY YOU DON'T MEAN THAT!
HE NEVER LIKES TO PARTICIPATE, MISS PEACH, YOU KNOW THE TYPE...
-IN THE SWIMMING CLASS HE'S A NON-SWIMMER...
-ON THE TRACK TEAM HE'S A CINDER-SCATTERER...
-IN THE GLEE CLUB HE'S A LISTENER!
YOU FORGOT THE DRAMATIC SOCIETY.
-I'M THEIR BEST TREE.
MELL

MARCIA, THE CLASS IS VERY ANXIOUS TO HEAR ABOUT THE PARADE YOU SAW YESTERDAY.
WHO COULD SEE?
-THERE WAS SUCH A CROWD, ALL I COULD SEE WAS THE FEATHER IN THE BANDLEADER'S HAT!
-BESIDES, THE DRUMS AND BUGLES GAVE ME A HEADACHE...
—IT WAS ALTOGETHER A REAL WASTE OF TIME!
WAS IT A NICE FEATHER?
MELL
ISN'T WOODCRAFT FUN, CHILDREN?
YES, BUT WE'RE NOT VERY GOOD AT BUILDING THINGS!
THAT'S OKAY... IF IT LOOKS TOO GOOD, IT'S NOT REALLY WOODCRAFT!
NOBODY WOULD BUY AWFUL LOOKING CHAIRS LIKE THESE...
OF COURSE NOT. THERE'S NO MARKET FOR SLOPPY, BADLY-MADE, INFERIOR PRODUCTS!
THERE ISN'T?
THEN HOW'S A GUY LIKE ME SUPPOSED TO MAKE A LIVING?
MELL

AHHH! THIS IS "THE GOOD LIFE"!
WHAT'S "THE GOOD LIFE"?
OH, FISHING, SWIMMING, BOATING... -THAT'S PART OF "THE GOOD LIFE".
-DOING WHATEVER WE LIKE...
FEELING FREE, HAPPY, ALIVE! THIS IS IT!
HERE COMES ARTHUR. HEY, ARTHUR! DID YOU EVER LIVE "THE GOOD LIFE"?
I WOULDN'T KNOW IT IF I FELL OVER IT.
MELL

I THOUGHT A HAYRIDE WOULD BE FUN...
I GUESS IT WOULD BE IF WE DIDN'T SINK IN LIKE THIS...
THIS HAY IS PACKED TOO LOOSE.
WHO LOADED THIS HAY?
I DID.
NEXT TIME PACK IT TIGHTER, STUPID.
MELL.

I'M SHAKESPEARE AND CONFUCIUS AND ARISTOTLE ROLLED UP IN ONE.
I'M SHAKESPEARE AND ER-UH-WHAT WERE THOSE OTHER TWO NAMES?
ECHO CANYON
ARTHUR'S ECHO IS EVEN DUMBER THAN HE IS.
MELL.
—THE NEXT QUESTION IS FOR YOU, ARTHUR. HOW WAS THE LAW OF GRAVITY DISCOVERED?
OUCH!
COULD YOU GIVE ME A HINT?
MELL.

THERE'S A **BEE!**
DON'T WORRY. IF YOU DON'T MOVE HE WON'T STING.
THAT'S TRUE BEES ONLY STING YOU IF YOU MOVE.
YES. **THAT'S THE RULE.**
OUCH!
YOUR TROUBLE, ARTHUR, IS THAT YOU'RE A NATURAL BORN EXCEPTION.
MELL.
"THE WORLD IS MY OYSTER." —WHAT DOES THAT MEAN, MISS PEACH?
IT'S AN EXPRESSION. ROUGHLY, IT MEANS EVERYTHING IS FINE; THE WORLD IS GOOD TO YOU AND IT'S YOURS FOR THE TAKING!
THE WORLD IS **MY** OYSTER!
MINE, TOO!
YOU **DON'T LIKE** OYSTERS, ARTHUR, SO YOU'RE OUT OF LUCK!
IS THAT *SO?* WELL, THE WORLD HAPPENS TO BE MY HAMBURGER!
MELL.

TEENAGERS SURE HAVE RESPONSIBILITIES THESE DAYS..!
MISS PEACH, ARE WE "TEEN-AGERS"?
NO, FRANCINE. "TEENAGERS" ARE CHILDREN BETWEEN 13 AND 19 YEARS OF AGE!
WELL, ARE WE "TODDLERS"?
NO! WE'RE "TOTS"!
WE'RE "TYKES"!
HECK NO! WE'RE "KIDDIES"!
DON'T YOU CARE WHAT WE ARE, ARTHUR?
NO THE SOONER WE'RE CLASSIFIED, THE SOONER THEY'LL FIND THINGS FOR US TO DO...
MELL
- AND THAT ENDS OUR ORAL TEST FOR TODAY CHILDREN!
ARTHUR GOT TWO ANSWERS RIGHT OUT OF TEN!
TWO OUT OF TEN!
TWO RIGHT AND EIGHT WRONG!
EIGHT WRONG AND TWO RIGHT!
WILL YOU TELL YOUR PARENTS, ARTHUR?
SURE! WHY SHOULDN'T I BRING A LITTLE SUNSHINE INTO THEIR LIVES?
MELL

YOU MUSTN'T LAUGH AT ARTHUR, CLASS. WE ALL MAKE MISTAKES...
name Three Planets.
IVY PLANET
CACTUS PLANET
TULIP PLANET
MISS PEACH IS RIGHT...
ARTHUR'S NO DIFFERENT THAN ANYONE ELSE...
-HE'S GOT THE SAME BRAINS AS WE HAVE...
SURE! -HE WAS LAUNCHED SUCCESSFULLY...
-HE JUST NEVER QUITE GOT INTO ORBIT...
MELL

ARTHUR, YOU ANSWERED THAT DIFFICULT QUESTION VERY WELL!
IMAGINE THAT!
THAT WAS A WONDERFUL ANSWER, ARTHUR...
-AREN'T YOU PROUD OF IT?
GEE! I WISH I COULD HAVE IT STUFFED OR SOMETHING...
MELL

-YOU'RE "TIRED OF WASTING YOUR TIME?"
YES, MISS PEACH! THIS COUPON MAY BE THE KEY TO A NEW AND RICHER LIFE...
YES!! -NOW'S OUR CHANCE TO TRAIN AT HOME FOR A HIGH PAYING PROFESSION THAT OPENS UP A WORLD OF OPPORTUNITY...
RIGHT!! -ONE IN WHICH WE WILL EARN BIG MONEY AND GAIN PRESTIGE FOR YEARS TO COME!!
WHO SAYS SO?
"READER J. B. C., OF BIRDSBORO, OHIO!".. -THAT'S WHO!!
-AND IF IT'S GOOD ENOUGH FOR A FAMOUS MAN LIKE HIM, IT'S GOOD ENOUGH FOR US!
MELL
FALL IS THE NICEST TIME OF THE YEAR.
YES, IRA! IT'S SO COLORFUL AND LOVELY...
AND NOTICE HOW THE WIND TAKES THE LEAVES AND SWIRLS THEM AROUND IN BEAUTIFUL LITTLE EDDIES AND WHIRLPOOLS!
WHERE? I CAN'T SEE A THING.
MELL.

-YOU SEE THE MORAL IN THIS?
YES, NEVER EAT JELLY SANDWICHES IN THE FALL.
MELL.

HEY! IT'S STARTING TO SNOW!
REMEMBER LAST WINTER? EVERYTIME IT SNOWED, ARTHUR GOT LOST ON HIS WAY TO SCHOOL!
LOST IN THE SNOW! HOW FOOLISH HE LOOKED!
YES! HE GOT LOST SO OFTEN, HE WAS THE LAUGHING STOCK OF THE SCHOOL!!
REMEMBER, ARTHUR? REMEMBER HOW DUMB YOU WERE ABOUT GETTING LOST?
YES. THIS TOO, IS GOING TO BE A VERY EMBARRASSING WINTER...
MELL.

I STILL DON'T BELIEVE THE WORLD IS ROUND!!
I STILL DON'T BELIEVE THE WORLD IS ROUND!!!
ECHO CANYON
ARTHUR LIKES ECHO CANYON...
-HE CAN BE TWICE AS STUPID WITH THE SAME EFFORT.
MELL
DEAR! POOR ARTHUR HAS GOTTEN LOST AGAIN ON HIS WAY TO SCHOOL.
WHERE IS THAT BOY?! WHY SHOULD HE GET LOST EVERYTIME WE HAVE A LITTLE SNOW?
HE ONLY LIVES THREE BLOCKS FROM HERE!
KEEP TALKING... -I'M COMING IN ON THE BEAM...
MELL

WHAT IS FRANCINE WORRIED ABOUT?
WHEN SHE GETS MARRIED, HER MOTHER BECOMES HER HUSBAND'S MOTHER-IN-LAW, RIGHT?
—AND THEN HER MOTHER BECOMES HER CHILDREN'S GRANDMOTHER...
—SO, MY PROBLEM IS, WILL MY MOTHER STILL BE MY MOTHER?
HOW SILLY! OF COURSE SHE WILL!
—OF COURSE! A GOOD LAWYER CAN FIX IT UP...
MELL
THE CHILDREN ARE DISAPPOINTED BECAUSE THEY COULD ONLY RAISE 35 CENTS FOR THE PRINCIPAL'S BIRTHDAY GIFT...
—SO MISS CRYSTAL IS TRYING TO CHEER THEM UP, EH?
CHILDREN! I HAVE A FINE IDEA FOR OUR PRINCIPAL'S GIFT!
—GIVE HIM A SCHOOL FULL OF HAPPY FACES...
—CLASSROOMS BUZZING WITH ACTIVITY... —AND AN AUDITORIUM FILLED WITH ENTHUSIASM!
CAN WE GET ALL THAT FOR 35 CENTS?
MELL

-AND SO, CHILDREN, I SHALL ALLOW MISS PEACH TO TAKE YOU ALL ON A TRIP TO NEW YORK CITY DURING CHRISTMAS WEEK!
GOODY!! -THE EMPIRE STATE BUILDING!
-THE STATUE OF LIBERTY!
-ROCKEFELLER CENTER!
I'M SO THRILLED! WE'VE BEEN STUDYING ABOUT NEW YORK ALL WEEK!!
THE EIFFEL TOWER!
MELL
DEER SANTA:
I HAVE BEEN A VERY GOOD, KIND BOY ALL YEAR, SO PLEASE BRING ME ELECTRIC TRAINS AND A NEW PARAKEET AND A BIKE AND A MAGIC SET AND A COWBOY SUIT. -AND ANYTHING ELSE YOU THINK I NEED.
-ALSO BRING MISS PEACH SOME NICE TOYS. SHE IS MY SCHOOL-TEACHER, SO THEY MUST BE SENSIBLE TOYS.
ALSO BRING MY FRIENDS MARCIA AND FREDDY AND STUART AND IRA AND SHEILA AND LESTER AND FRANCINE SOME TOYS, TOO. THEY ARE GOOD KIDS AND I KNOW THEY LIKE ME, OR THEY WOULDN'T LAUGH AT ME
SO MUCH. BUT SANTA, IF YOU DON'T HAVE ENOUGH TOYS FOR ALL OF US, DON'T FEEL BAD. I WILL LET THE OTHERS PLAY WITH MY TOYS EVERY OTHER TUESDAY BETWEEN 3 AND 3:30. THE REASON I AM SO GENEROUS IS I AM PRACTISING TO BE YOUR HELPER WHEN I GROW UP. IT'S A GOOD "CAREAR-FEILD" BECAUSE IT IS NOT "CROWDED."
I HOPE YOU WILL KEEP ME IN "MIND" FOR THIS JOB. (HAVE ROSY CHEEKS, "WILL" TRAVEL.)
LOVE, ARTHUR
MELL

-SO THIS IS NEW YORK! GOODNESS-IT MAKES MY HEAD SPIN, MISS PEACH!
EAST SIDE AIRLINES TERMINAL
IT'S SO CROWDED AND BUSTLING, MISS CRYSTAL...
HONK! HONK!
CLANG!
BEEP! BEEP!!
-HOW MANY FOLKS LIVE HERE, STUART?
EIGHT MILLION!! EIGHT MILLION PEOPLE!!
I HOPE I'M MAKING A NICE IMPRESSION ON THEM...
MELL
NEW YORK IS A VERY BIG CITY, CHILDREN. LET'S STAY TOGETHER SO NO ONE WILL GET LOST!
SPEAKING OF LOST. WHERE'S ARTHUR?
-HE WAS WITH US A WHILE AGO..
OH, DEAR!! WHERE CAN HE BE?.
-HE'LL PROBABLY MEET US AT OUR HOTEL...
MELL
-IF HE HAS ENOUGH SENSE TO ASK A POLICEMAN FOR DIRECTIONS...
PARDON ME, POLICEMAN, -COULD YOU DIRECT ME TO...
GO AWAY, SONNY, YOU BOTHER ME...
-IMMEDIATE SEATING IN ALL PARTS OF THE BALCONY!!

-IRA AND ARTHUR ARE PLAYING A WORD GAME?
"BABBLE", MISS PEACH.
-SO FAR THEY'RE NECK AND NECK...!
(SIGH!) THERE'S NOTHING LIKE A CONTEST BETWEEN TWO EXPERTS.
IMPOSIBEL
WHITCH
MELL.
THE MAN WHO INVENTED STAPLES WAS A GENIUS!
-YES! THEY HAVE SO MANY PRACTICAL USES!
-YOU CAN STRAIGHTEN ONE OUT AND USE IT FOR A TOOTHPICK...
-OR YOU CAN PLAY A SHORT-RANGE DART GAME, WHERE SPACE IS LIMITED...
-BUT ARTHUR'S IDEA IS THE BEST! -A CARRYING HANDLE FOR A PENCIL!
-YES. IT'S FOR ARTISTS WHO TRAVEL...
MELL.

IMAGINE ARTHUR REFUSING TO JOIN THE "SILVERWARE SQUAD"...!
YOU KNOW HIM... HE DOESN'T PARTICIPATE IN **ANYTHING.**
SOMETIMES I WONDER WHY HE EVEN BOTHERS TO COME TO SCHOOL....
—HE JUST TAKES UP SPACE, —THAT'S ALL...
OH, LOOK AT THAT SWEET LITTLE BOY!
DO YOU GO TO SCHOOL, SONNY?
YES, BUT NOT ACTIVELY.
MELL.
HAVE YOU COUNTED THE VOTES, MARCIA?
WELL! —IT SEEMS THAT **ARTHUR** HAS BEEN ELECTED **"WASTE-BASKET MONITOR"!**
SAY! THAT'S **WONDERFUL!**
ISN'T THAT **GRAND!**
CONGRATULATIONS. ARTHUR!
LOTS OF LUCK!
WOULD YOU CARE TO SAY A FEW WORDS, ARTHUR?
WELL, I WANT TO THANK YOU FOR YOUR CONFIDENCE, AND I PROMISE THAT I WILL DO MY VERY, VERY LEVEL BEST AND I'LL DEVOTE ALL MY BRAINS TO DOING A GOOD JOB WITH THE WINDOW POLE...
—WASTE-BASKET, ARTHUR...
ARTHUR'S CAMPAIGN HEADQUARTERS
CAMPAIGN MANAGER, FREDDY.
MELL

KELLY SCHOOL AUDITORIUM
DID YOU ENJOY THE SHOW, CLASS?
OH, YES, MISS PEACH! THAT "PUNCH AND JUDY" SURE ARE FUNNY!
—THEY'RE A RIOT!! —THE SILLY THINGS THEY DO!!
YOU LOVED THE "PUNCH AND JUDY", DIDN'T YOU, ARTHUR?
YES, I ALWAYS HAVE.
—YOU SEE, THEY'RE MY KIND OF FOLKS.
—THEY'RE STUPID.
MELL.
DO YOU BOYS PLAN TO GO TO COLLEGE SOMEDAY?
I CERTAINLY DO, MR. MUSSELMAN. I'M AN EXCELLENT STUDENT.
YOU NEED REAL GOOD MARKS TO GET INTO COLLEGE...
YES, AND THE ENTRANCE EXAMS ARE VERY HARD...
HOW WILL YOU EVER GET INTO COLLEGE, ARTHUR?
—A BASKETBALL SCHOLARSHIP, I GUESS.
COACH
MELL

CHILDREN, HAVE YOU NOTICED HOW CLEAN THE ROOM IS SINCE ARTHUR HAS BEEN WASTE-BASKET MONITOR?
GEE, I HADN'T REALLY NOTICED..!
ARTHUR, YOU'RE THE UNSUNG HERO OF THE WASTE-BASKET..!
I THINK IT'S HIGH TIME ARTHUR GOT SUNG. DON'T YOU, CLASS?
YES!
ARTHUR, ARTHUR ARTHUR, ARTHUR ARTHUR, ARTHUR
MELL
-THEY SAY THERE'S MORE TO AN ICEBERG THAN MEETS THE EYE. WHY, MISS PEACH?
THAT'S BECAUSE NINE-TENTHS OF IT IS HIDDEN, UNDER WATER...
GEE. -LOTS OF THINGS IN LIFE ARE LIKE THAT...
-MAYBE THAT'S THE WAY IT IS WITH POOR ARTHUR...
-YOU MEAN NINE-TENTHS OF HIS ABILITY IS HIDDEN, HUH?
NO! -SHE MEANS NINE-TENTHS OF HIS BRAIN IS UNDER WATER...
MELL

MISS PEACH IS YOUR TEACHER...
—WE ARE YOUR CLASSMATES...
—MISS CRYSTAL IS THE TEACHER NEXT DOOR...
—AND I AM MR. GRIMMIS, YOUR PRINCIPAL.
OH. I THINK I'VE GOT IT NOW...
MELL.
GOODNESS—YOU'VE MADE A GIANT **SNOW STATUE** OF ARTHUR!
YES, MISS PEACH...
—IT'S A MONUMENT TO ARTHUR!
THAT'S A STUPID MONUMENT!
WELL, HE'S MONUMENTALLY STUPID, ISN'T HE?
MELL.

A Star for Miss Crystal

In every red-blooded American school there come moments when the faculty, or a representative thereof, must be made to appear ridiculous.

For just such moments we have Miss Crystal, who by so lending herself keeps Miss Peach's dignity intact.

And for this, I love her and hereby award her a Star, two Pine Trees and a George Washington.

MISS CRYSTAL WILL JOIN US HERE IN A WHILE FOR OUR NATURE LESSON, CHILDREN.
GOODY, MISS PEACH! LET'S IDENTIFY BIRDS WHILE WAITING!
THERE'S A LONG-CRESTED BLUE JAY-BIRD!
-AND AN ASH-THROATED FLYCATCHER
-AND A WHITE-RUMPED WESTERN SHRIKE!
THERE GOES A LONG-TAILED ENGLISH MAGPIE!
-AND HERE COMES A BIG-NOSED, LONG-LEGGED AMERICAN SCHOOL-TEACHER!
MELL
DON'T YOU TEACHERS THINK THAT WORKING HERE AT KAMP KELLY IS BETTER THAN, SAY, A SUMMER CRUISE?
YES, SIR, MR. GRIMMIS! WORKING OUT WITH THE KIDS HERE IS VERY HEALTHY! WOULDN'T GET MUCH EXERCISE ON THE QUEEN MARY!
I'M VERY HAPPY, MR. GRIMMIS! THIS SUMMER AT KAMP KELLY IS FAR MORE REWARDING THAN AN OCEAN CRUISE. DON'T YOU AGREE, MISS CRYSTAL?
Z-Z-Z
Z
Z-Z-ZORK!? HUH?? DECK TENNIS, ANYONE?
MELL

WHAT'S GOING ON?
THE **SCHOOL BOARD** HAS ASKED OLD MISS CRYSTAL TO **RETIRE...** —FOR THE **FIFTH** TIME...
—AND, AS USUAL, SHE CHALLENGED THE CHAIRMAN TO A **JUDO MATCH...**
—AND, AS USUAL, SHE'S **WINNING...**
—AND, AS USUAL, YOU MAY FORGET ABOUT **—OOOOOF!** —RETIRING!
MELL.
TSK, TSK. POLICEMEN, FIREMEN, PLUMBERS...
MISS CRYSTAL NEEDN'T HAVE BOTHERED...
—CERTAINLY NOT... —THE SWINGS AND SEE-SAWS ARE FUN ENOUGH FOR ME!
POLICE EMERGENCY
DEMONSTRATING MONKEY BARS IS NOT PART OF YOUR JOB, MISS CRYSTAL.
MELL

—AND ONCE AGAIN MISS CRYSTAL WILL BE HONORARY QUEEN OF THE KELLY SCHOOL WINTER CARNIVAL!
—WHY CAN'T ONE OF US YOUNGER WOMEN BE "QUEEN" THIS YEAR?
YES! —WHO NEEDS MISS CRYSTAL?
—WELL, I THINK MISS CRYSTAL SHOULD BE "QUEEN" AGAIN...
LESTER'S RIGHT! —WE DON'T NEED HER, BUT SHE'S SORT OF TRADITIONAL...
SURE! —LIKE A WITCH AT HALLOWE'EN..
MELL
WHAT'S HAPPENED, CHILDREN?
COAC
NOTHING SERIOUS, MISS PEACH...
—MISS CRYSTAL WAS SHOWING US HOW SHE USED TO POLE-VAULT...
DON'T JUST STAND THERE GAPING... GET ME DOWN!
MELL

Bulletin Board Jungle

Arthur's responsibilities are few, and they're carefully chosen to allow for his limitations. It'll be a cold day when they let <u>him</u> fire up the furnace, for instance. But even an idiot can manage a bulletin board.

ARTHUR'S IN CHARGE OF THE BULLETIN BOARD, MISS PEACH..
-AND LOOK WHAT A MESS IT IS!
IT'S CLUTTERED AND SLOPPY...
A COMPLETE DISGRACE!!
KAMP KELLY BULLETIN BOARD
NOTICE
BUT IT'S NEWSY, ISN'T IT?
MELL
-THAT'S A VERY IMPORTANT NOTICE!
YES! IT MUST BE BROUGHT TO THE IMMEDIATE ATTENTION OF EVERYONE IN THE SCHOOL!
GRACIOUS! PUT IT ON THE BULLETIN BOARD, ARTHUR!!
—WELL, IF ITS SO ALL-FIRED IMPORTANT, I GUESS I WILL...
KELLY SCHOOL BULLETIN BOARD
NOTICE
MELL

WHY WEREN'T YOU AT THE MEETING OF THE "NEATNESS SQUAD" YESTERDAY, LESTER?
I DIDN'T KNOW THERE WAS A "NEATNESS SQUAD" MEETING...
THE NOTICE WAS POSTED FOR ALL TO SEE...
—SURE! WHY DO YOU THINK ARTHUR MAINTAINS A BULLETIN BOARD....
BULLETIN BOARD
NOTICE
—AS A DECORATION, OR SOMETHING?!
MELL
DIDN'T ARTHUR CLEAN OFF THAT DISGUSTING BULLETIN BOARD YET?
YES, MR. GRIMMIS. —HE DID.
YES, MR. GRIMMIS. —I DID.
KELLY SCHOOL BULLETIN BOARD
NOTICE
THEY SHOULDN'T BLAME ARTHUR... BULLETIN BOARDS JUST GET THAT WAY...!
YES, BUT IN TWO DAYS?!
MELL

ARTHUR!
HAVE YOU CLEANED OFF THAT DISGRACEFUL BULLETIN BOARD OF YOURS YET?
KELLY SCHOOL BULLETIN BOARD
YES MR. GRIMMIS, BUT WHAT SHOULD I DO WITH THIS?
NOW THAT YOUR BULLETIN BOARD HAS BEEN CLEARED OFF, ARTHUR...
KELLY SCHOOL BULLETIN BOARD
I'M GOING TO WATCH IT AND SEE...
KELLY SCHOOL BULLETIN BOARD
HOW IT GETS SO MESSY..
KELLY SCHOOL BULLETIN BOARD
-SO FAST!?!
KELLY SCHOOL BULLETIN BOARD

The Green Bird of Happiness

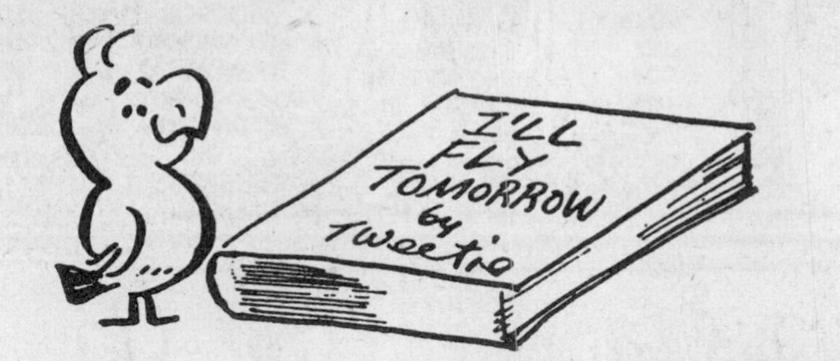

Arthur's pet parakeet, Tweetie, took off on February 15th, 1957, and hasn't been seen since. Arthur's classmates are convinced he'll never return, but Arthur has dedicated himself to finding the erudite little bird who needs his help like Charles Van Doren needs Private Doberman's.

All in all, it's the terribly sad story of a parakeet and his lost boy.

IT WAS NICE OF ARTHUR TO BRING HIS **PARAKEET** TO SCHOOL TODAY!
I DON'T THINK SO. HE WAS A SHOWOFF.
HE WASN'T A SHOWOFF. HE WAS ONLY TRYING TO ENTERTAIN US.
IT TALKED NICELY. DID YOU HEAR IT SAY "HELLO, DARLING"?
YES, BUT IT'S A SHAME ARTHUR HAD TO GO AS FAR AS HE DID...
IF HE HAD SIMPLY **TOLD** US HIS PARAKEET WAS **VERY TAME** WE WOULD HAVE BELIEVED HIM...
SURE. HE DIDN'T HAVE TO TRY AND **PROVE** IT.
?
HOW MANY BIRDS CAN YOU RECOGNIZE, CHILDREN?
THERE'S A **CHICKADEE.** HE'S A FRIENDLY, HAPPY BIRD!
THE **NUT HATCH** CLINGS UPSIDE DOWN WHILE LOOKING FOR INSECTS!
I RECOGNIZE THE **TOWHEE.** HE NESTS ON THE GROUND...
...AND A NOISY OLD **JAYBIRD**...!
THERE'S AN INTERESTING BIRD- IT LOOKS JUST LIKE MY **PARAKEET** THAT FLEW AWAY LAST YEAR!
HELLO, ARTHUR! HOW ARE THINGS AT HOME?
WELL

IS ARTHUR STILL UPSET BECAUSE HIS PARAKEET FLEW AWAY?
YES MISS PEACH. HE'S BEEN **SULKING** SOMETHING **AWFUL...**
IT'S A **TERRIBLY SAD** SITUATION...
SAD? IT'S **HEART BREAKING!** LET'S CHIP IN AND BUY HIM A NEW ONE.
SURE! A NEW PARAKEET ONLY COSTS **EIGHT DOLLARS!**
WOULDN'T IT BE **CHEAPER** TO LOOK FOR **A LITTLE HUMOR** IN THE SITUATION?
MELL

ARTHUR'S PARAKEET HAS BEEN MISSING SINCE FEBRUARY.
-AND NOW THE POOR KID THINKS IT'S HIDING IN THE WOODS...
WAS A PARAKEET'S LIFE REALLY **THAT** BAD?
-WELL, THE **BABY TALK** WAS BAD ENOUGH...
-BUT BETWEEN THE **VITAMIN BIRD SEED,** AND THE **"BIRD-EE-TOYS"** IT WAS **HORRIBLE!**
TSK, TSK! WHEN WILL PEOPLE REALIZE THEY HAVE TO STOP DOING THINGS FOR THE BIRDS?
MELL.

ARTHUR IS STILL PINING FOR HIS MISSING PARAKEET?
YES, MISS PEACH. NOW THE POOR KID THINKS IT DOESN'T WANT TO COME BACK...
SANCTUARY! SANCTUARY!!
BIRD SANCTUARY
MELL
THE CHILDREN ARE TRYING TO RAISE MONEY TO BUY ARTHUR A NEW PARAKEET.
HOW MUCH HAVE YOU SO FAR?
7 CENTS MISS CRYSTAL...
—BUT FREDDY'S TAKING OVER THE FUND RAISING.
—AND HE'S A PROMOTIONAL GENIUS.
GIVE THIS BOY A BIRD
MELL

ARTHUR'S PARAKEET IS STILL MISSING?
YES, MISS PEACH. THE POOR BOY HASN'T SEEN IT IN EIGHT MONTHS!
—AND WHAT'S MORE HE HASN'T EVEN HEARD FROM IT...
(SOB!) —IF I ONLY HAD SOME WORD FROM MY PARAKEET...
(GASP!) WHICH ONE OF YOU IS ARTHUR?..
—I BRING WORD FROM YOUR PARAKEET!
MELL
WHAT IS ALL THE EXCITEMENT ABOUT, CHILDREN?
ARTHUR'S PARAKEET!
DON'T TELL US HE'S COME BACK?
NO, BUT ARTHUR HAS FINALLY HEARD FROM HIM!
HELLO, ARTHUR. HOW ARE THINGS AT HOME?
OH. HOW NICE! HE SENT YOU A PHONOGRAPH RECORD!
MELL

WHY DOES ARTHUR STILL MISS THAT PARAKEET OF HIS?
WELL, HE'S ATTACHED TO HIM!
SURE! HE LOVES THAT BIRD!
-THAT'S EASY TO UNDERSTAND. YOU PROBABLY EVEN **TAUGHT HIM TO TALK**, DIDN'T YOU, DEAR?
WORSE!! HE WAS IN THE FAMILY FOR TEN YEARS, MISS PEACH...
-**HE** (SOB!) TAUGHT **ME** TO TALK!!
MELL.
WHAT'S NEW, TWEETIE?
WELL, THE CLOVERS BEAT THE TIGERS, 9-5... -THE MAYOR SAYS TAXES WILL GO UP THIS YEAR...
DOES HE **REALLY** TALK?
(SIGH!) YES, I DO. WHAT WOULD YOU LIKE ME TO SAY?
4 X 3 = 12, ARTHUR... 5 X 3 = 15, 6 X 3 = 18, 7 X 3 = 21...
WHO NEEDED IT?
MELL.

Weeds are only Human

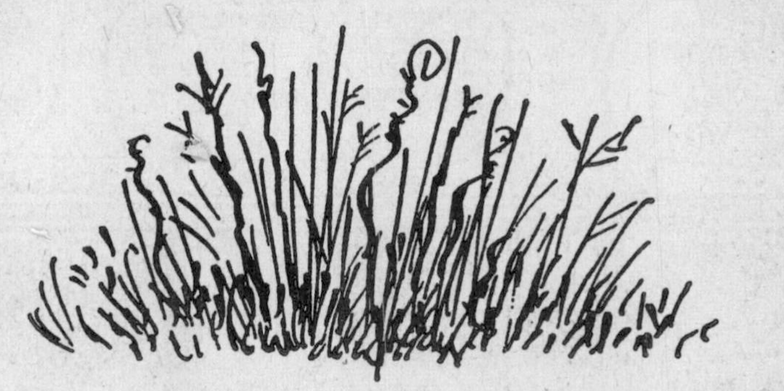

Weeds are human just like any other plant, so Arthur figures they deserve to be cultivated and loved. Actually, his affinity for weeds is due to the fact that Arthur himself is a weed in the garden of life.

AND WHAT KIND OF A GARDEN IS MISS PEACH'S CLASS GROWING?
WEEDS. -STRICTLY WEEDS!
WEEDS? ALL THESE PLANTS YOU'RE CULTIVATING ARE WEEDS?
NOBODY LIKES WEEDS, BUT WE LIKE 'EM!
WEEDS CAN BE VERY NICE IF YOU GIVE THEM HALF A CHANCE.
SURE! WEEDS ARE HUMAN, JUST LIKE ANY OTHER PLANT..
MELL
KELLY SCHOO AL FLOWER SHOW
IT'S HARD TO RAISE PRETTY FLOWERS... MISS PEACH,
YES! WEEDS ARE THE BIGGEST PROBLEM...
-YOU'VE GOT TO KEEP ALERT AND PULL OUT THE WEEDS THE MOMENT THEY APPEAR...
—IT'S A CONSTANT STRUGGLE— WEEDS VS. FLOWERS.
—SOMETIMES THE WEEDS ACTUALLY WIN...
YES... IF YOU'RE NOT ON YOUR TOES...
1
2
3
5
6
FRANCINE
IRA
MARCIA
SHEILA
LESTER
ARTHUR
MELL

WHAT IS ARTHUR DOING IN THE GARDEN?
GARDENING.
IN THE FALL?
ARTHUR, DON'T YOU KNOW THAT PEOPLE DO THEIR GARDENING IN THE SPRINGTIME?
THAT'S THE BEAUTY PART OF WEEDS...
—THEY'LL GROW ANY OLD TIME.
MELL.

ARTHUR HAS INVITED US TO SEE HIS **WEEDHOUSE** MISS PEACH!
UGH! **WHAT AN OVERGROWN MESS!**
—EVEN **WEEDS** SHOULD BE KEPT NICE AND NEAT, ARTHUR!
—DON'T YOU TAKE CARE OF THEM, ARTHUR?
—THAT'S WHY I INVITED YOU OVER...
—I'M AFRAID TO GO IN THERE ALONE...
ARTHUR'S
MELL.

IT'S ALMOST THREE O'CLOCK!
IT'S TIME TO GO HOME, ARTHUR DEAR. YOU'VE BEEN WORKING ALL AFTERNOON...
ARTHUR'S STILL IN WITH HIS WEEDS, MISS PEACH.
WHO'S WORKING?
-I'VE BEEN LOST IN HERE SINCE LUNCHTIME...
BY THE WAY... -HELP.
MELL
FLOWERS ARE NATURE'S GIFT OF BEAUTY.
YES, THEY'RE GORGEOUS!
WHAT ON EARTH IS ARTHUR DOING?
-OH, HE'S CURLING HIS WEEDS!
-CURLING YOUR WEEDS, ARTHUR?
YES, MISS PEACH...
-WEEDS NEED ATTENTION, YOU KNOW...
-DID YOU THINK THEY WERE NATURAL BEAUTIES?
MELL
2-28

Muscles vs. Lester

When you're an underweight kid like our Lester, who cares that Metropolitan Mutual considers you a Class A risk? You want muscles and lots of bulk.

To the Lesters of America: Take heart! Some day, when you grow up and are writing those quarterly premium checks, you'll be glad you hardly tip the scales. In the meantime, laugh when the bullies on the beach kick sand in your face.

MR. MUSSELMAN SAYS I HAVE A POWERFUL BUILD!
ME TOO! PLENTY OF BEEF AND GOOD, STRONG MUSCLES!
LESTER IS SKINNY! LOOK HOW SKINNY HE IS!
HAR! HAR! THE HUMAN PIPE CLEANER!
LESTER, YOU'RE NOTHING BUT SKIN AND BONES!!
OH YES? SKIN AND BONES AND GOOD, STRONG VEINS!
COACH
MELL

FEEL THOSE MUSCLES TINGLE, MEN... -THAT BLOOD COURSING THROUGH YOUR VEINS!
1-2-3 1-2-3
COACH
YES SIR, MR. MUSSELMAN! IT FEELS GREAT!
BRACING!
I REALLY FEEL ALIVE!
ME TOO!
ISN'T IT GREAT TO BE ALIVE, LESTER?!
WELL, IT'S A NOVELTY.
MELL.

WHAT'S AN X-RAY?
KAMP KELLY X-RAY ROOM
IT ENABLES THE DOCTOR TO SEE THAT EVERYTHING IS IN ORDER INSIDE OF YOU.
(GULP!) —IF IT'S NOT DO THEY MAKE YOU TIDY UP?
MY, BUT YOU'RE THIN, LESTER! WHEN WILL YOU GET SOME MEAT ON THOSE BONES?
YOU WON'T HAVE TO X-RAY LESTER, DOCTOR...
—NO, SIR. JUST HOLD HIM UP TO A STRONG LIGHT!
MELL.
NOW THAT THE SUMMER IS ALMOST OVER, DID CAMP AGREE WITH YOU, FELLOWS?
COACH
I GAINED 3 POUNDS AND GREW 2 INCHES!
I GAINED 1½ POUNDS AND GREW 1 INCH!
I GAINED 7 POUNDS AND GREW 1½ INCHES!
I LOST 2 POUNDS AND SHRUNK 3 INCHES!
-CAMP DIDN'T AGREE WITH ME.
MELL

-LESTER IS TAKING SOME MUSCLE-BUILDING EXERCISES?
YES MR. MUSSELMAN. WHENEVER LESTER GOES TO THE BEACH, BULLIES PICK ON HIM...
YES! -AND I'M TIRED OF HAVING SAND KICKED IN MY FACE!
-THE EXERCISES WORK, TOO! HE'S ACTUALLY GETTING MUSCLES IN HIS ARMS!
-AND BY NEXT SUMMER, IF BULLIES KICK SAND IN HIS FACE AGAIN...
-HE'LL HAVE THE STRENGTH TO RAISE HIS ARMS AND COVER HIS EYES...
COACH
MELL
WHAT ON EARTH IS WITH YOU, LESTER?
I'M TAKING A MUSCLE-BUILDING COURSE!
WHY, YOU NINNY.. -YOU HAVEN'T MADE AN OUNCE OF PROGRESS!
-YOU'RE JUST AS SKINNY AND WEAK AS YOU EVER WERE...
-SKINNIER, EVEN...
NOW YOU GAVE THE KID AN INFERIORITY COMPLEX..
MELL

Science since Sputnik

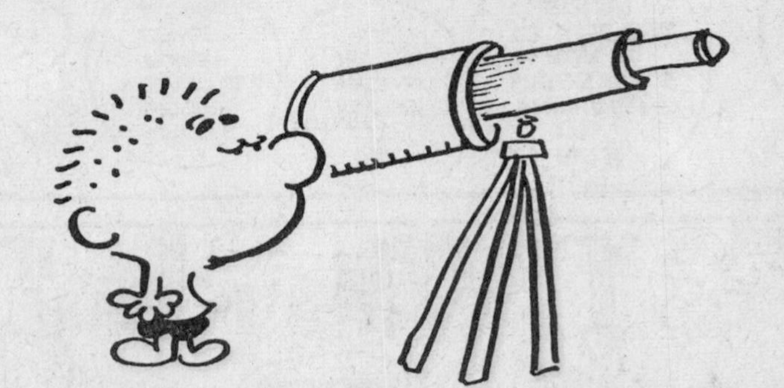

Science used to be cute, but since Sputnik it's become a pretty serious business.
In the great International Scientific Brains Game, Miss Peach's crew is our ace in the hole.
They prove conclusively that where Science is concerned, you <u>can</u> start too young.

THE CHILDREN REALLY SEEM TO ENJOY THE SCIENCE LAB. MR. GRIMMIS!
THEY'VE CERTAINLY THROWN THEMSELVES INTO IT ...!
DO YOU KNOW US SCIENTISTS CAN MAKE RAIN AND SNOW? —EVEN DIAMONDS?
IMAGINE! NATURE DOES THOSE THINGS, TOO!
WHO NEEDS NATURE?
-US SCIENTISTS ALWAYS GOT ALONG VERY NICELY WITHOUT IT, THANK YOU...
SCIENCE NEWS
MELL,
OUR SOLAR SYSTEM HAS NINE PLANETS THAT REVOLVE AROUND THE SUN!
ONLY NINE?
—SUPPOSE ANOTHER NICE LITTLE PLANET COMES ALONG...
—COULDN'T IT REVOLVE AROUND THE SUN, TOO?
NO!! IT'S PHYSICALLY IMPOSSIBLE FOR IT TO JOIN OUR SOLAR SYSTEM!!
STUART ALWAYS WAS A SNOB.
MELL,

WHAT KIND OF BOOK ARE YOU READING, CHILDREN?
IT'S **SCIENCE FICTION.** MISS PEACH...
—AND TALK ABOUT **SCARY!**
—IT SAYS THAT SOME DAY THE **EARTH** WILL **STOP** SPINNING.
-AND WHEN THAT HAPPENS WE'LL ALL **FLY OFF INTO SPACE AND FLOAT AROUND FOREVER!**
—SO WHAT? A CHANGE OF PACE NEVER HURT ANYBODY...
MELL.

—BUT WHY SHOULD THAT **SCIENCE FICTION STORY** FRIGHTEN YOU, CHILDREN?
IT SAYS THE (SOB!) **WORLD COULD END.** MISS PEACH...
"—THE EARTH COULD STOP SPINNING, AND GET HOT FROM THE SUN...
—AND EXPLODE INTO (GULP!) **A MILLION PIECES!"**
AREN'T **YOU** WORRIED ABOUT **THE END OF THE WORLD, ARTHUR??**
HECK NO.
—I'VE GOT MY OWN TROUBLES.
MELL.

CHILDREN, I INSIST UPON KNOWING WHAT YOU ARE DOING!
IT'S A SECRET, MR. GRIMMIS...
-YOU'LL SEE IT WHEN IT'S READY...
-AND WON'T YOU BE PROUD OF US!
AHEM! -IN THE MEANTIME, MISS CRYSTAL...
-YOU'RE STANDING ON OUR LAUNCHING PAD...
MELL.
(YAWN!) ARTHUR SEEMS FASCINATED BY THE PLANETS...
ASTRONOMICAL OBSERVATORY
(SIGH!) -HE'S BEEN STARING AT MARS FOR AN HOUR NOW...
I THINK IT'S WONDERFUL!
ARTHUR DEAR, ARE THERE ANY QUESTIONS YOU'D LIKE TO ASK?
YES, MISS PEACH... WHAT ON EARTH IS THAT?
MELL.

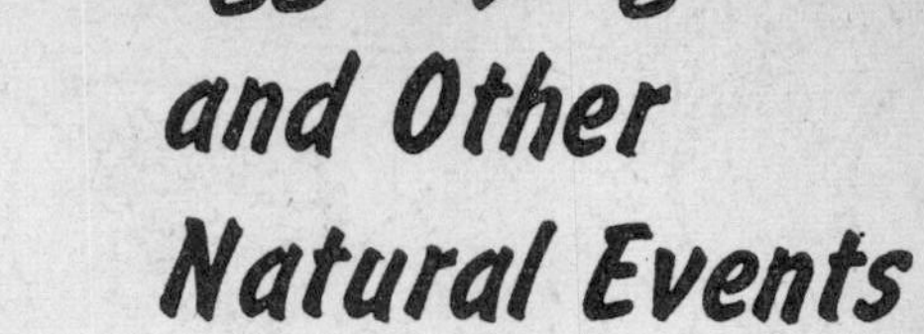

Egg-laying and Other Natural Events

In merely one Nature Period per day, Miss Peach's class clearly demonstrates the growing popularity of egg-laying among nature's creatures, as well as the lack of courtesy shown by bees who don't wipe their feet on your flowers.

The world around us isn't really so complex, now, is it?

I'M RAISING **SWEET WILLIAM** FOR THE CLASS.
THESE WILL BE **PETUNIAS!**
THESE ARE YOUNG **ROSE BUSHES.**
EVERYBODY LOVES **CROCUSES.**
THE WHOLE SCHOOL WILL LOVE MY **VIOLETS!**
I'M GROWING **LILIES-OF-THE-VALLEY.**
THESE ARE **IRISES.** WE GREW SOME AT HOME LAST SUMMER AND WE ENJOYED THEM. EVERYONE IN CLASS WILL ENJOY THEM.
THIS IS **POISON IVY.** I FINALLY BECAME IMMUNE TO IT LAST SUMMER AND I HOPE TO DO THE SAME FOR THE REST OF THE CLASS...
MELL
THESE FISH LAY THEIR EGGS AMONG THE PLANTS...
EGGS? ONLY **BIRDS** LAY EGGS!
NOT JUST BIRDS! **FISH** AND **BUGS** DO, TOO...
-AND A CERTAIN MAMMAL, THE **PLATYPUS,** LAYS EGGS!
-AND **FROGS** LAY EGGS...
HOW COME IT'S GETTING SO POPULAR?
MELL

SOMETHING AWFUL HAPPENED, MISS PEACH!
-ARTHUR IS MONITOR OF THE MAGNOLIA BLOSSOM...
-AND HE DIDN'T WATER IT YESTERDAY!
OH, HOW CAN YOU POSSIBLY EXPLAIN THIS, ARTHUR!?
I FORGOT
BESIDES, I'M TOO YOUNG TO BE RESPONSIBLE FOR AN ENTIRE MAGNOLIA BLOSSOM.
MELL

YOUR PLANTS ARE DOING WONDERFULLY, STUART!
THAT BOY HAS A GREEN THUMB!
YES INDEED!
-AND LOOK AT IRA'S TROPICAL FISH! THEY'RE CERTAINLY THRIVING!
YES INDEED. I HAVE WHAT YOU CALL A WET THUMB.
MELL

IF I GOT LOST, MISS PEACH, I WOULDN'T KNOW WHICH DIRECTION IS WHICH!
IT'S SIMPLE, FRANCINE!.. -IF YOU WALK TOWARDS THE PACIFIC OCEAN, YOU'RE GOING WEST...
-BUT IF YOU WALK TOWARDS THE ATLANTIC, THAT'S EAST.
-OR WAIT 'TIL THE STARS COME OUT AND LOOK FOR POLARIS. THAT'S NORTH...
-OR, IF YOU CAN HOLD OUT 'TIL FALL, NOTICE WHICH WAY THE BIRDS FLY...
-AND THAT'S SOUTH.
MELL
THIS IS A STATUE OF A DODO BIRD, CHILDREN.
DODO BIRD
SILLY ARTHUR SAYS HE SAW A FLOCK OF THEM FLYING SOUTH LAST FALL!
HA! HE COULDN'T HAVE! EVERYBODY KNOWS THEY'RE EXTINCT!
AMERICAN BIRDS
THAT MEANS THEY'RE NO LONGER WITH US!
I KNOW, I KNOW! I SAW THEM LEAVING...
MELL

KELLY SCHOOL FLOWER SHOW
HAVE YOU SEEN ARTHUR'S DAISY?
IT'S GORGEOUS!
YOU'VE NEVER SEEN A DAISY LIKE ARTHUR'S...,
-IT'S A REAL BEAUTY!
-HE'LL CERTAINLY WIN THE LOVING CUP IN THE DAISY DIVISION!
--I'LL WIN THE LOVING CUP; I WON'T WIN THE LOVING CUP; I'LL WIN THE LOVING CUP; I WON'T WIN THE LOVING CUP; I'LL WIN THE....
MELL

THAT BEE WAS DRINKING NECTAR FROM OUR FLOWERS, CHILDREN.
YES, MISS PEACH. HE GOT POLLEN ON HIS FEET...
-AND NOW HE'LL FERTILIZE ANOTHER FLOWER WITH THE POLLEN!
IN ANOTHER GARDEN?
AT SOME OTHER CAMP?
HUMPH!
I WISH BEES THAT DRINK OUR NECTAR WOULD HAVE THE COURTESY TO WIPE THEIR FEET ON OUR FLOWERS!-
MELL

KAMP KELLY NATURE ROOM
SNAILS ARE FUNNY-LOOKING!
YES, BUT THEY'RE USEFUL. THEY KEEP THE AQUARIUM CLEAN.
—BUT WHEN THERE ARE TOO MANY THEY'RE A NUISANCE, HUH?
(SOB!) THAT'S US WOMEN: "THE SNAILS IN THE AQUARIUM OF LIFE"...
TODAY'S DUTY:
FRANCINE
MARCIA
SHEILA
CLEAN & SWEEP NATURE ROOM.
MELL.
LAKE KELLY
WHEN I'M FLOATING, I FEEL VERY CAREFREE!
WELL, I'M NERVOUS!
—I'VE BEEN READING ABOUT THE DREAD PIRANHA FISH!
(GULP!) THE LITTLE FISH WITH THE BIG TEETH?
DON'T WORRY! THE PIRANHA ONLY EATS SMALL ANIMALS!
-BESIDES, THEY LIVE IN SOUTH AMERICA!
—AFTER SWIMMING THAT FAR, THEY'D BE HUNGRY ENOUGH TO EAT ANYTHING!
NOW I'M NERVOUS!
MELL

PET ANIMALS NEED CARE, ATTENTION, AND MOST OF ALL, LOVE!
KAMP KELLY NATURE CLUB
I LOVE THEM, MISS PEACH. SMACK!
I LOVE THEM, TOO. SMACK!
ME, TOO! SMACK!
DON'T WORRY, KID. I'LL MAKE IT UP IN CARE AND ATTENTION...
MELL.

-SINCE YOU BROUGHT THE PLANTS IN FOR THE WINTER, CHILDREN, THERE IS NO ROOM IN HERE FOR ANYTHING ELSE... -CAN'T YOU TAKE SOME OF THEM HOME?
ARTHUR IS MONITOR OF THE PLANTS...
-WHAT DOES HE THINK?
I'LL FIND OUT...
ARTHUR, ARE YOU HERE TODAY?
MELL.

CONGRATULATE LESTER, MISS PEACH...
Bless Our Home Room
-HE'S JUST BEEN ELECTED "PLANT-TURNER"!
"PLANT-TURNER"?
YES!
YOU KNOW HOW PLANTS ALWAYS GROW TOWARD THE SUN?.
-WELL, I'LL HAVE TO TURN THEM A FEW TIMES A DAY...
-SO THEY WON'T GROW UP ROUND SHOULDERED...
MELL
THE MOTHER SQUIRREL LOOKS SO ALERT, DOESN'T SHE, CLASS?
NATURE
YES. -AND HER FUR IS SO PRETTY.
IT SAYS HERE: "THE MOTHER SQUIRREL IS CLEVER, INDUSTRIOUS AND THRIFTY"...
-SO HOW COME SHE'S NOT WEARING MINK?
MELL

The Liveliest Arts

The question is which art is the liveliest around here—what with art, dancing, and the Kelly School Dramatic Society in full flower.

One day, I'm aghast as I watch the Society rewrite Shakespeare "so that he makes a little sense." But the next day I warm with gladness to realize that practically every family blessed with female children harbors a Pavlova.

MELL
FABULOUS!
IT'S TRULY AMAZING! SUCH TALENT AT HER AGE!
YOU MEAN LITTLE FRANCINE DID THIS?
SUCH EXPRESSION- SUCH FORM- MAGNIFICENT!
"A CHICKEN" By FRANCINE
IT WAS SUPPOSED TO BE A CHICKEN, BUT FREDDY (SOB) DROPPED IT ON THE FLOOR AND STOMPED ON IT... THEN HE (SOB) TOOK IT AND THREW IT AT MY HEAD...
MELL
2-26
HOW IS OUR CLASS PROJECT COMING ALONG?
FINE, MISS PEACH. IT'S A REAL PEACEFUL COUNTRYSIDE.
-ON A LAZY SUMMER AFTERNOON.
-WITH THE SUN SHINING BRIGHT.
-AND THE COWS MOOING GENTLY IN THE PASTURE.
-AND THE KIDDIES PLAYING QUIETLY.
-AND THE BIRDS WHEELING NOISELESSLY OVERHEAD.
-AND THE FARMER BOY SLEEPING PEACEFULLY IN THE HAY.
-YES-IT'S A SHAME TO SPOIL IT WITH THESE UGLY DERRICKS, BUT THEY STRUCK OIL -AND BUSINESS IS BUSINESS!

YOU SHOULDN'T USE ALL THOSE COLORS, IRA! DUCKS ARE SUPPOSED TO BE YELLOW!
DUCK by IRA
THAT MUST BE THE KIND OF DUCK THAT FLIES TO THE SOUTH RIGHT, IRA?
WHY IS ARTHUR CRYING IN THE CLOSET? ALL I SAID WAS: "SINCE WHEN DOES A HIPPOPOTAMUS HAVE ALL THOSE CRAZY COLORS?"
I DON'T THINK YOU SHOULD HAVE CRITICIZED HIM. HE'S SENSITIVE.
HIPPOPOTAMUS by ARTHUR
(SOB!) THAT'S RIGHT! BESIDES, (SOB!) THAT MIGHT BE THE KIND OF HIPPOPOTAMUS THAT FLIES TO THE SOUTH!
MY PAINTING IS CALLED "A LITTLE GIRL WALKING IN THE SUN."...
—MINE IS CALLED "A LITTLE BOY WALKING IN THE SUN"...
—THIS IS "A LADY WALKING IN THE SUN"...
-I CALL MINE "A MAN WALKING IN THE SUN"...
IRA'S LOOKS VERY ORIGINAL! IT'S IMPRESSIONISTIC, ISN'T IT?
YES, MISS CRYSTAL! IT'S CALLED "A WHOLE FAMILY WALKING IN THE SUN"...
MELL

ISN'T OUR WINDOW BEAUTIFUL?
WE'VE DECORATED IT WITH CUTOUTS!
I'M SO PROUD, I COULD CRY!
SAY! YOU SHOULD SEE WHAT MISS CRYSTAL'S CLASS DID NEXT DOOR!
NOW THIS IS A WINDOW!
GEE! IT'S GREAT! SIMPLY GREAT!
I'M SO IMPRESSED I CAN HARDLY SPEAK!
WONDERFUL! WONDERFUL! PUT ON THE LIGHTS SO WE CAN SEE IT BETTER...
MELL.
DID YOU SEE THE WONDERFUL PICTURE IRA DREW, MISS CRYSTAL?
OH, IT'S LOVELY!
MARVELOUS!
IRA, YOU'RE A REGULAR REMBRANDT!
OH, I WOULDN'T SAY THAT...
-REMBRANDT WAS TWICE THE ARTIST I AM.
MELL.

MELL
I AM THE SUN - SHINE - SHINE - SHINE...
I MAKE THE DAY -FINE -FINE -FINE...
WE ARE THE RAINDROPS -DROP -DROP -DROP...
WE ARE BLADES OF GRASS -POP -POP -POP...
MISS RODGERS?
MISS HAMMERSTEIN!
MELL
POCAHONTAS AND JOHN SMITH
WASN'T MY CLASS PLAY SCHEDULED FOR TODAY, MISS CRYSTAL?
NO DEAR. MINE WAS!
KING ARTHUR AND THE KNIGHTS OF THE ROUND TABLE

DANCE OF THE SEVEN FIREFLIES
MELL

—BUT WHY AM I ALWAYS THE RAINDROP?
YOU'RE NOT! IN OUR LAST PLAY YOU WERE A TREE...
...AND BEFORE THAT YOU WERE A MAILBOX...
...AND ONCE YOU WERE AN AZALEA BUSH.
WHY COMPLAIN? —AT LEAST YOU GET A VARIETY OF ROLES!
—SURE! —WHAT KIND OF PARTS DO WE PLAY?
PEOPLE, PEOPLE, PEOPLE!
Casting Today.
MELL

WHAT PLAY ARE YOU GOING TO PUT ON CHILDREN?
HAMLET, MISS PEACH.
WE FIXED IT UP A LITTLE SO THAT IT MAKES SENSE.
KAMP KELLY DRAMATIC SOCIETY
TO PLAY OR NOT TO PLAY, THAT IS THE QUESTION. WHETHER 'TIS NOBLER IN THE MIND TO SAVE MY MARBLES— OR TO TAKE UP MARBLES AGAINST A SEA OF MARBLE-SHOOTERS, AND BY OPPOSING—BEAT THEM— TO WIN THE THOUSAND NATURAL MARBLES THAT FREDDY IS HEIR TO, —'TIS A CONSUMMATION DEVOUTLY TO BE WISHED!—TO PLAY MARBLES— PERCHANCE TO LOSE—AY!— THERE'S THE RUB...
MELL.
"THIS IS MO-MENT MU-SICAL
THIS IS MO-MENT MU-SICAL
THIS IS MO-MENT MU-SICAL
COM-POSED BY FRANZ SCHU-BERT..."
"BAR-CA-ROLE;
FROM TALES OF HOFF-MAN
WRITTEN BY OFF-ENBACH..."
"THIS IS THE SYM-PHONY
THAT SCHU-BERT WROTE
BUT NE-VER FI-NISHED...."
THE MUSIC IS NO GOOD, BUT THE WORDS ARE CATCHY...
MELL.

SEE THE LIT-TLE BIRDIES, FLYING IN THE SKY...
-SEE THE LIT-TLE BIRDIES, FLYING OH SO HIGH...
-ON DAINTY LIT-TLE WINGS THEY GLIDE SO MERRI-LY...
-HEAR THE LIT-TLE BIRDIES TWEE-TWEE-TWEE...
-TWEE TWEE..
-TWEE TWEE..
-TWEE TWEE..
(PSST!) CAN YOU BRING ARTHUR BACK? HE PUT ON THE WRONG COSTUME...
MELL
WHEN THE SUN IS A-ROPIN' ON THE RIM O' THE HILL...
AND THE DOGIES ARE RUSTLIN' AND THE WIND BLOWS STILL...
AND THE EVER-LOVIN' SAGEBRUSH IS A-SINGIN' A SONG...
AND THE CAYUSE IS A-HERDIN' THE CANYON ALONG...
AND THE ROLLIN' HILLS LASSOO THE BUNKHOUSE TRAIL...
AND THE...
KELLY SCHOOL VARIETY SHOW
The Three Tumbleweeds
MISS PEACH, THAT'S OUR SONG THEY'RE SINGING.
NO IT ISN'T, DEAR. ITS DIFFERENT!
"THE TUNE-TOTIN' TRIO"
WELL, IT SOUNDS LIKE OUR SONG.
MELL

KELLY SCHOOL DRAMATIC SOCIETY
THAT'S THE TROUBLE WITH YOU AND YOUR **PROP DEPART MENT...**
YOU HAVE TO BE **THANKED** FOR EVERY LITTLE THING...!
MELL
MISS CRYSTAL, I **STILL** THINK IT WAS A GOOD IDEA TO LET THE CHILDREN CONDUCT THEIR OWN **MUSIC APPRECIATION** CLASS
HI, ALL YOU CRAZIES OUT THERE IN RECORD LAND! THIS IS IRA, YOUR FAVORITE "D.J." SPINNING THE OLD PLATTERS TO YOU AND YOU AND YOU. OUR NEXT NUMBER, KIDDIES, IS FOR "MARCIA AND SHEILA"; FOR "THE GANG OVER AT THE WINDOW"; FROM "L.H." TO "M.P."; FOR "STUART AND FRANCINE"; FOR "THE TWO TEACHERS STANDING IN THE DOORWAY"; AND FOR "FREDDY, ARTHUR AND ALL THE BOYS DOWN THERE AT THE WATER FOUNTAIN"...
HERE IT IS, KIDDIES—TSCHAIKOWSKY'S "1812 OVERTURE"...
MELL

MARCIA'S WRITTEN A KELLY SCHOOL FIGHT SONG?
YES, MISS PEACH! -IT'S A SWELL ONE!
ARE YOU SURE IT'S ORIGINAL, MARCIA?
KELLY
-PLAY IT AND DON'T ASK SO MANY QUESTIONS.
MELL
KELLY "YALE BOOLA!"
by A. M. HIRSH
© LEO FEIST, INC.
KELLY, KELLY KELLY, KELLY, KELLY, KELLY
KELLY, KELLY KELLY, KELLY, KELLY, KELLY
HAVE YOU CAST THE PART OF RIP VAN WINKLE YET, CLASS?
CASTING TODAY "RIP VAN WINKLE"
IT'S A DIFFICULT CHOICE, MISS PEACH....
-IRA, HERE, HAS TALENT, EXPERIENCE AND POISE...
-WHILE ON THE OTHER HAND, ARTHUR'S HALF-ASLEEP TO START WITH...
MELL

ARTHUR FELL ASLEEP RIGHT IN THE MIDDLE OF THE FIRST ACT...
Z
—AND THAT'S THE LAST TIME **HE** GETS A LEAD PART...
Kelly School Art Players PRESENT "RIP VAN WINKLE"
MELL,
-IS EVERYTHING READY FOR THE **EASTER PLAY,** MARCIA?
YES, MISS PEACH.. WE'RE HAVING ONE MORE DRESS REHEARSAL.
ON STAGE, BUNNIES AND EGGS!
WHY SO DEEP IN THOUGHT, ARTHUR?
I WAS JUST PUZZLING, MISS CRYSTAL...
WHICH DO YOU SUPPOSE CAME FIRST....
—THE RABBIT OR THE EGG?
MELL.

WHAT DID YOU BRING TO 'SHOW AND TELL' TODAY, CLASS?
I SHOW YOU THIS RARE PIECE OF JAVANESE SCULPTURE, AND I WILL NOW TELL YOU ABOUT IT; THEY SAY IT IS THE ONLY ONE OF IT'S KIND IN AMERICA, AND MY UNCLE HAS ALLOWED ME TO SHOW IT TO YOU. IT IS MOST·INTERESTING· AND I'M SURE YOU WILL AGREE IT IS VERY RARE. THANK YOU.
THAT'S RARE, ALL RIGHT. MY 'SHOW AND TELL' IS JUST THIS SHIP MODEL. IT'S NOT NEARLY AS INTERESTING AS WALTER'S SCULPTURE.
WALTER'S THING IS SO NICE, I DON'T EVEN WANT TO TALK ABOUT MY 'SHOW AND TELL.'
ME NEITHER. MINE IS NOTHING COMPARED TO WALTER'S RARE AND MARVELOUS SCULPTURE.
MELL
IS THAT AN AIR RAID SIREN I HEAR?
NO, MR. GRIMMIS, -A BUNCH OF LISTENERS WERE JUST PROMOTED TO HUMMERS!
HUMMMMMMMMMMMMMMMM
OH, KELLY SCHOOL, WE CHERISH THEE WE HOPE THAT THERE SHALL E'ER BE · THY HALLOWED HALLS AND IVY'D WALLS AND ALL LIKE THAT...
KELLY SCHOOL GLEE CLUB

Mom and Pop

Kids have big mouths. If you think your child is cute when he tells you the foolish things his teachers say, try imagining what your own foibles sound like to the teachers.

WHY DID YOU ALLOW THE TWINS TO BRING ALL THEIR TOYS TO CAMP, MISS CRYSTAL ?
MR. GRIMMIS, THE POOR KIDS BEGGED ME ! IT SEEMS THERE'S A BIG BULLY IN THE CITY WHO MONOPOLIZED ALL THEIR TOYS DURING THE YEAR...
THAT'S RIGHT ! THE TWINS SAY HE NEVER LET THEM PLAY WITH THEIR OWN TOYS !
THAT'S DISGRACEFUL ! HOW OLD IS THE BULLY?
HOW OLD IS. DADDY ? 39 OR 40?
MELL.
MY YEARS AS A GYM TEACHER HAVE MADE ME THE STRONGEST MAN IN THE WORLD!
KAMP KELLY
MY FATHER IS STRONGER, MR. MUSSELMAN...
HE SAYS HE HAS HIS BOSS ON HIS NECK ALL DAY.
MY DAD'S EVEN STRONGER. HE SAYS HE'S BEEN CARRYING MY UNCLE FOR YEARS.
MY MOTHER SAYS EVERY, NEW YEAR'S EVE MY DADDY TAKES ON THE BIGGEST LOAD SHE'S EVER SEEN.
MY FATHER MUST BE VERY STRONG.. -GRANDMA SAYS HE EVEN HAS MUSCLES IN HIS HEAD!
MELL

ARTHUR TOLD AN UNTRUTH AND EMBARRASSED THE ENTIRE CLASS! HE SAID HIS MOTHER IS "TWENTY-ISH."...
-SO WE ENTERED HER IN THE "YOUNGEST MOTHER CONTEST."...
- AND IT TURNS OUT SHE'S THIRTY YEARS OLD!
"TWENTY-ISH," INDEED!!
WHY DIDN'T YOU TELL US YOUR MOTHER IS THIRTY YEARS OLD?
WELL, WHAT DO YOU THINK "ISH" MEANS?
MELL

DON'T FORGET TO SHOW YOUR PARENTS THE PICTURES YOU DREW, CLASS!
I HATE THAT BUSINESS! IT'S A FARCE!
IT SURE IS! -MY MOTHER WILL SAY: "OH, WHAT A BEAUTIFUL MASTERPIECE!"
-MY FATHER WILL COME HOME AND SAY: "MARVELOUS! MY BOY'S A GENIUS!"
-THEY'LL CALL IN ALL THE NEIGHBORS, WHO'LL SAY: "WHAT A WONDERFUL TALENT!"
-BUT TRY TO GET THEM TO SPEND TWO DOLLARS FOR A FRAME...
MELL

DID YOU ALL BRING IN YOUR PARENT'S CONSENT NOTES FOR CAMP, CHILDREN?
YES MISS PEACH!
HERE'S MINE...
-AND MINE!
-HOW COME YOURS IS ALL TATTERED AND TORN, IRA?
MY MOTHER GAVE IT TO ME LAST SEPTEMBER.
MELL

YOU SAY YOUR FATHER BELIEVES IN **"THINKING BIG,"** IRA?
YES, MISS PEACH...
-HE SAYS THAT'S THE WAY TO GET AHEAD...
WHAT DOES THAT MEAN, "THINK BIG?"
-IT'S LIKE "MIND OVER MATTER"...
-**THINK** BIG AND YOU'LL **BE** BIG...!
THINK BEAUTIFUL, MISS CRYSTAL... **THINK** BEAUTIFUL...
MELL.

The Principal of the Thing

Regardless of what the kids will say, I'm going to wind up with the following tribute to Mr. J. W. Grimmis, principal of Kelly School. . . .

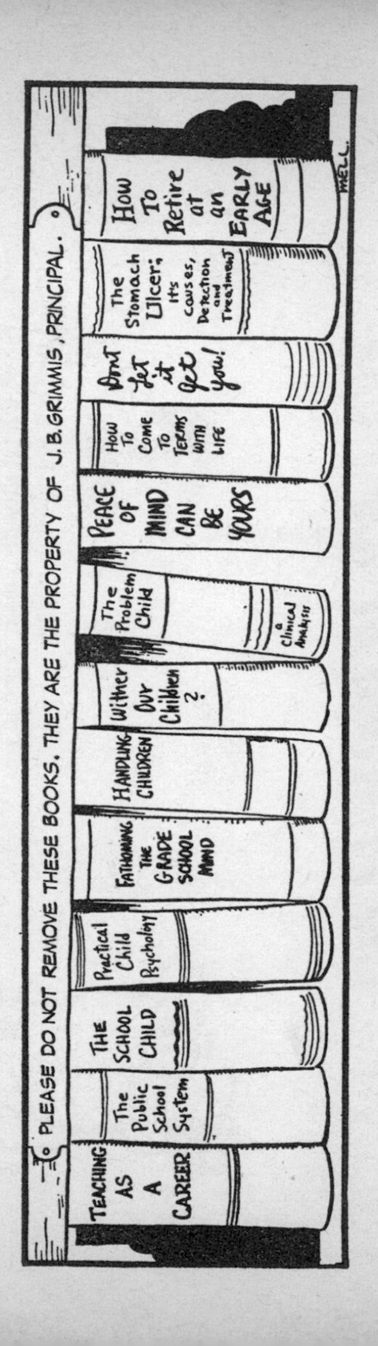
PLEASE DO NOT REMOVE THESE BOOKS. THEY ARE THE PROPERTY OF J. B. GRIMMIS, PRINCIPAL.
TEACHING AS A CAREER
The Public School System
THE SCHOOL CHILD
Practical Child Psychology
FATHOMING THE GRADE SCHOOL MIND
HANDLING CHILDREN
Wither Our Children ?
The Problem Child
a Clinical Analysis
PEACE OF MIND CAN BE YOURS
HOW TO COME TO TERMS WITH LIFE
Don't Let it Get You!
The Stomach Ulcer; It's causes, Detection and Treatment
How To Retire at an EARLY AGE